· A ·
GOOD·BOOK
· IS THE ·
PRECIOUS
LIFE-BLOOD
· OF A ·
MASTER
SPIRIT
Milton

PRINTED IN GREAT BRITAIN

The KINGS TREASURIES
OF LITERATURE

GENERAL EDITOR
Sir A·T· QUILLER COUCH

LONDON : J·M·DENT & SONS LTD.

HOMER

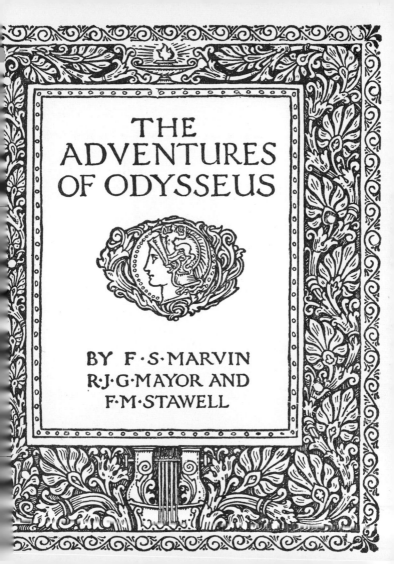

THE ADVENTURES OF ODYSSEUS

BY F·S·MARVIN
R·J·G·MAYOR AND
F·M·STAWELL

CONTENTS

CONTENTS

INTRODUCTION

THE stories told in this book and its companion volume are taken from the *Iliad* and the *Odyssey*, two of the greatest poems of ancient Greece. The Greeks believed that in early times their country had been inhabited by a race of men stronger and wiser than themselves, whom they called the Heroes, and they thought that in those days the Gods whom they worshipped used to appear on earth and take part in the doings of men. Tales of the Gods and Heroes were told in poems and dramas, and were represented in carvings on the temples and in paintings on vases, such as those from which the pictures in this book are taken. The most famous of them all was the story of the Trojan War, part of which is told here.

The war began through a wrong done by Paris, son of Priam the Trojan king. He had carried off the most beautiful woman in Greece, Helen, wife of Menelaus, and the Greek Heroes sailed to Troy under Agamemnon, king of Mycenae and brother of Menelaus, to punish the deed. But the Trojans refused to give back Helen, and the siege of Troy was long and hard. The *Iliad* tells of the battles round the walls and of the great chiefs who fought there, among whom was Odysseus, the wisest of them all, and Nestor, the old orator, and Ajax, whom Odysseus saw again in the House of Death. It tells, above all, of the quarrel between Agamemnon and Achilles, the bravest of the Greeks; and how Achilles withdrew from the fight in anger, and how trouble came to him and he repented, and how he slew Hector, the noble son of Priam and the champion of Troy, and how he learnt to honour his foes.

Other poems carried on the story to the fall of Troy. Achilles and Paris and many more heroes on either side were killed, but at last the Greeks got within the walls through a stratagem of Odysseus mentioned in the *Odyssey* (chap. iv. and chap. viii.). He had a great wooden horse made and set up on the shore, and the Greeks pretended it was an offering to the goddess Athena. But it was hollow inside, and Odysseus himself with a chosen band was hidden there. And the Trojans were deceived and took it into the city and put it in Athena's temple. Then at night Odysseus and his men came out from their hiding-place and opened the gates to their comrades. Thus the Greeks took the town and burnt it, and Menelaus carried Helen home again. But the return was often difficult for the heroes. Troy lay across the sea, the war had lasted ten years, and much had changed at home in their absence, so that many tales were told of their adventures on the journey back or at their home-coming. Odysseus was the last of all to return, and he found strangers troubling his wife Penelope, and trying to steal his kingdom for themselves. The *Odyssey* tells of this.

The time at which the siege of Troy was said to have taken place was long before the Greeks began to write history. But discoveries have been made of late years in Greece and the countries round it, which show that there were cities in very early days such as the poems describe, and that man must have lived much in the way they represent. At Mycenae there have been found the remains of walls and gates and graves of kings, and in the graves ornaments worked in gold, like the brooch which Odysseus wore (*Odyssey*, chap xix.), and weapons inlaid in the style magnified by the poet who describes the wonderful shield of Achilles (*Iliad*, chap. XI.). On the site where Troy was said to have stood, by the sea-shore near the Dardanelles, explorers have found traces of dwellings that must be many centuries old, and in especial the ruins of one strong city with well-built walls and towers. In Crete they have found the remains of palaces still more magnificent, which belong to the same or an earlier period, and it may be that some features of that ancient civilisation are reflected by the life of the Sea Kings in the *Odyssey*.

The Greeks believed that both the *Iliad* and the *Odyssey* were composed by a blind old man named Homer, who wandered about from place to place and sang his songs at festivals. Other singers learnt the poems by heart, and so they were handed on from one generation to another. Later, when writing became common, they were carefully written down, and grew to be better known in Greece than any other book. Children learned to read them in the schools; they were recited on holidays, and the people never tired of hearing them; the wisest men studied and reverenced them, and the greatest poets found in them subjects for their plays.

Our versions only attempt to give in shortened form the outlines of the two great stories. It must never be forgotten that the originals are poems of a beauty which no translation can represent.

It should be noted that the " Greeks " did not describe themselves by that name. At the time to which these poems refer they knew themselves as " Achaians " or " Argives."

It may also be well to explain that the Greek vase-painters did not consider themselves bound to follow in every detail the stories they illustrated. This is how it comes about that Eumaeus appears in the scene with Odysseus and the old nurse (p. 165), and that the women are seen standing behind Odysseus at the slaying of the suitors.

Most of the illustrations have been drawn by Mrs. Stewart, to whom we owe our warmest thanks for her beautiful work. We have also to thank the authors and publisher for their kind permission to use some of the plates from *Greek Vase-Paintings* (J. E. Harrison and D. S. MacColl. Fisher Unwin).

In each volume will be found a Pronouncing List of the difficult proper names, and a brief Appendix on the Homeric Problem.

F. S. M.
R. J. G. M.
F. M. S.

PALLAS ATHENA

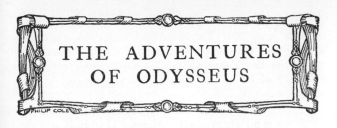

THE ADVENTURES OF ODYSSEUS

CHAPTER I

HOW ATHENA PLEADED FOR ODYSSEUS IN THE COUNCIL
OF THE GODS AND OF THE TROUBLES AT HIS
HOUSE IN ITHACA

Sing us the song of the hero, steadfast, skilful, and strong,
Taker of Troy's high towers, wanderer ten years long,
Over the perilous waters, among strange lands and men,
Leading his comrades onward, seeking his home again.
Sing us the song of the Wanderer, sing us the wonderful song!

IT was ten years since the Greeks had taken Troy,
and all the heroes who had escaped from the war and
the perils of the sea were safe at home again in
Greece. Odysseus alone had never returned, and
was left to waste his soul in Calypso's island, far
away from Ithaca, his native land. But Father Zeus
had determined that he should reach his home at
last, though he was not to be free of trouble even
there; and all the Gods pitied him, except Poseidon,
the lord of the sea, who wished him ill and raged
against him continually, for he had his own cause
of spite.

13

Now one day Poseidon had gone to visit the Ethiopians who dwell at the ends of the earth, and the other Gods were sitting together on Olympus, in the hall of Zeus, and speaking of the fate of mortal men.

"They blame us," said Father Zeus, "and say that we send them their evil lot. But it is not so. It is their own blindness and wickedness that work their ruin."

Then Athena spoke, the wise Goddess with the clear grey eyes: "Father and king, some men, it is true, deserve their fate. But what of Odysseus? My heart is torn when I think of him, pining away in that lonely island where Calypso dwells, the daughter of Atlas, the wizard who knows all the secrets of the sea and guards the pillars that keep heaven and earth apart. She holds him there and woos him with soft and winning words. But his one desire is to reach his native land again, were it only to see the smoke curling up from the roof of his house. Will the lord of Olympus let him die? How can he be wroth with Odysseus, after all the sacrifices he offered on the spreading plains of Troy?"

And Zeus replied, "No, my child, I could never forget Odysseus, the wisest man on earth. But Poseidon is wroth with him, ever since he blinded his son, the giant Cyclops. And so he keeps him away from Ithaca and will not let him reach his home. But if we are all agreed, Odysseus shall return in spite of this, for one God cannot strive alone against the rest, and Poseidon must give up his wrath."

Then she answered, " If such is the will of the Gods, let Hermes, the messenger, go to Calypso and tell her our decree. But I will go to Ithaca and arouse Telemachus, Odysseus' son, and bid him call an assembly and speak out against the princes, who are devouring his father's substance and wooing his father's wife. Then I will send him to Pylos and Sparta to seek tidings of Odysseus there."

So saying, she bound on her beautiful sandals that bear her like the wind over sea and land, and shot down from the heights of Olympus to the house of Odysseus in Ithaca. There she took the shape of a prince called Mentes, a friend of his, and went up to the palace and stood in the gateway, with her bronze spear in her hand.

The courtyard was strewn with the hides of the oxen that had been slaughtered for the feast, and the princes were lying upon them and playing at draughts, while the banquet was being prepared. Their henchmen were busy in the hall, washing the tables and mixing the wine and carving the joints of meat.

Telemachus was in the courtyard too, sitting among the princes, dreaming of his father and wondering if he would ever return and scatter them all and come into his own again. He was the first to notice the Goddess, and he rose at once and went out to meet her, for he could not bear to think that a stranger should be kept standing at the gates. So he took her by the hand and greeted her warmly and led her into the hall. He put her spear against a pillar in a polished stand where the spears of Odysseus stood, and gave her a beautiful carved chair in a quiet corner of the hall, and sat down beside her

himself. Then a maid-servant brought a silver basin and poured water over their hands from a golden ewer, and another loaded a table with all kinds of bread and meat. The princes came in after them to their feast, and when it was over they made Phemius take his lyre and sing to them.

But Telemachus and Athena were sitting apart close together, and talking low, so that the others could not hear. "Stranger," said Telemachus, " those men are light of heart and love the lyre and song, for they are devouring another man's substance and paying nothing for all they take. And his bones, maybe, are rotting on some distant shore or floating on the waves. Ah! if they saw him home again, they would pray for speed of foot sooner than all the gold and raiment in the world. But he will never come now. I would not believe it, even if some one told me that he was on the way. But tell me now who you are yourself and how you came here. Is it your first visit, or are you an old friend of my father's, for he had many guests?"

Then the Goddess replied, "My name is Mentes, and I am an old friend of your house. I am on a voyage to Cyprus, to buy copper in exchange for iron. If you would know more of me, ask old Laertes, your father's sire. His life is sad now, I hear, and he stays alone on the farm-land with one old servant and never comes to the city. I thought to find your father here when I came and, though he is so long delayed, I believe with all my heart that he will soon come back. He must be kept somewhere against his will, perhaps on an island in the far-off seas. But he would know how to find a way out, even if he were bound in iron chains. I am no seer, but I am sure of that. And so you are his son! I can see for myself how like you are. You have his head and his beautiful eyes that I remember so well in the old days, when we used to talk together before he set sail for Troy. We have never met since then. But come now, tell me, what is this rout I see? Can

these be guests of yours? How wantonly they revel
in your house!"

"Sir," said Telemachus, "it is the ruin of our
house that you see. My father is gone for ever, and
these men are the princes from Ithaca and the islands
around, who have come to demand my mother in
marriage. They destroy our wealth, but she will not
give them an answer; and so it goes on from day to
day, and I shall soon perish too."

Then the Goddess said, "Alas, poor son, how
sorely you need the mighty hand of your father to
right your wrongs. If he were only standing in the
doorway now with helmet and shield and spear as
I knew him in his prime! But listen and I will tell
you what to do. To-morrow summon all the lords
of Ithaca together, and there before the assembly
bid these men leave your house; and if your mother
desires to marry, let her return to her father's house
and be married thence. But for yourself, fit out a
ship, the best you have, and go to Pylos and to Sparta
to seek for news of your father. If he is still alive,
wait and endure this ruin for another year; but if
you hear that he is really dead, come home to build
him a funeral mound and pay him every honour,
and give your mother in marriage to one of the lords.
And now farewell, for I must be going, and remember
what I say. You are a child no longer and must
talk and act like a man."

Then Telemachus begged his guest to stay or at
least to take some worthy gift in memory of him.

But Athena would not wait. She rose and turned herself into an eagle and flew away over the sea. Then Telemachus knew that he had seen a Goddess, and took her words to heart and went back among the suitors, stronger and braver than before.

Now the minstrel was singing to them the sad story of the return of the Greeks from Troy and they were listening in silence, when Penelope the queen appeared, standing in the doorway, with her bright veil before her face. She had heard the song from her upper chamber and had come down weeping, to beg the minstrel for some other lay.

" Phemius," she said, " you know many other songs that charm the minds of men. But this one will break my heart, for it tells me of my dear lord, whom I mourn for day and night."

Then Telemachus said, " Mother, let the minstrel sing as he pleases. He is not to blame, but Father Zeus, who gives men joy and sorrow as he will and to us this grief. Be brave and listen, for all men love to hear the newest song."

Penelope was astonished as she heard him and went back to her room, and Telemachus turned to the princes and said, " Go on with your feast, proud lords, and be merry, if you will: I too delight to hear a minstrel who can sing us such songs as these. But in the morning I bid you all assemble in the public square, for I have a word to say. There I shall demand that you leave these halls and find your feasts elsewhere. And, if you refuse, I shall call on the Gods to repay you for all your crimes."

And the princes, too, were astonished when they heard him speak so boldly, and bit their lips; and Antinous, who was ever the foremost, said, " My lord Telemachus, you speak like a man inspired. It would be an ill day for us all, if Zeus made you king in sea-girt Ithaca, as your fathers were before you."

And Telemachus answered, " I will take the kingship gladly, if Zeus will give it me. But it may pass to some other lord, now that Odysseus is dead and gone. Only I claim for myself, and will maintain, the rule in my father's house."

Then another of the suitors, called Eurymachus, joined in, " Who shall be king of Ithaca, only the Gods can tell. But we are all content that you should keep your own possessions, Telemachus, and be master in your own house. But tell us, who was the stranger that came here just now? Did he bring any news of your father? He was gone so quickly that no one could see who he was. But he had a noble mien."

" I expect no more news of my father," said Telemachus, " and I have no faith in signs. That man was a prince called Mentes, a friend of our house."

But he knew in his heart that it was the heavenly Goddess, and when the song and the dance were done, he went to his own chamber to think over all she had said. And Eurycleia, the old nurse, went with him and lighted him to his room. She had nursed

him as a baby and no one in the household loved
him more. She waited there and took his doublet
and folded it up and hung it on a peg. Then she
went away and closed the door carefully behind her.
And he lay awake all night, wrapt in his soft sheep-
skin, and thinking of the journey that Athena would
have him make.

CHAPTER II

HOW TELEMACHUS SPOKE TO THE PEOPLE AND WENT IN SEARCH OF HIS FATHER

IN the morning the heralds called the assembly together, and Telemachus went down with his sharp sword slung about him and his spear in his hand and two fine dogs at his heels. He seemed a nobler figure than ever before, as he sat down in his father's seat, while all the elders made way for him and the people looked on in wonder.

Then one of the elders opened the debate, an old man bent with age. One of his sons had gone with Odysseus to Troy, and the loss was ever in his mind.

"Who has called us together?" he said. "It is the first time since Odysseus went to Troy. Has some brave man heard news of the absent host?"

Then Telemachus leapt up and stood in the midst of the assembly, and the herald put the speaker's staff in his hand and he began:

"Old man, it is I who have called this assembly together, but I have no public news. It is the ruin of my house that has made me do it, and of that I must speak. I have lost my father, who was a father to his people too, and now there are men, lords of these islands, who beset my mother in our house against her will and are afraid to go to Icarius, her father, and ask her in marriage from him. I am not strong enough to drive them out myself, and so they stay on and revel, and all our cattle are being slaughtered and the good wine drunk for naught. Friends, men of Ithaca, will you not hold them back for good Odysseus' sake and let me bear my grief alone? "

So saying, he dashed the staff to the ground and burst into tears; and all the people pitied him and for a while no one had the heart to speak.

At last Antinous made answer, " You are angry, Telemachus, and make bold to put the blame on us. But your mother herself must bear it, she who has led us on these four years and tricked us with her craft. No one could be more cunning. She sent secret messages to us all and gave every man some ground for hope; meanwhile she had a scheme at work which would defeat us all.

" She set up a great loom in the palace and began to weave a web upon it, fine and very wide. ' The lord Odysseus,' she said, ' is dead and gone, and all you noble suitors are eager to marry his wife. But you must wait and give me time to finish this shroud for his father, old Laertes, who is near his end. I should be disgraced among all the women of Greece, if for all his wealth he had no winding-sheet to lie in when he died.' And so we waited and she kept weaving this great web by day; but every night she came and unravelled it again. For three years she beguiled us thus; but in the fourth year one of her serving-women told us all, and we went in by night and found her there. So she was forced to finish it against her will.

"And now, Telemachus, before all this assembly, we make you answer. Either you must send your mother home and let her father choose whom she shall wed; or else we shall make suit to her still, and stay in your house and eat your substance, until she chooses for herself."

And Telemachus answered, "How can I send my own mother away from the house against her will? All men would blame me, and her father would seek to punish me, and she herself would pray for vengeance and Heaven would hear her prayer. No, leave my house yourselves, if you have any shame, and eat your feasts elsewhere. But if you still refuse, I call upon Zeus and all the Immortal Gods to punish you for your sins."

And as he spoke, Zeus sent down a sign from Olympus to show that his prayer was answered. Two eagles were seen flying overhead, grappling with one another and glaring down on the crowd below. And an old soothsayer interpreted the omen and said that Odysseus was already on his way home, bringing destruction to the suitors. But they derided him, and bade him go home and prophesy to his children or it might be the worse for him: they would go on with their wooing as they had begun.

Then Telemachus remembered the counsel of the Goddess and spoke again, " Princes, I will say no more about the wrong you do me, for now it is known to all men and to the Gods above. I only ask the people for a ship and twenty seamen, that I may go to Pylos and Sparta to seek for tidings of the king."

And after he had spoken Mentor arose, the faithful friend of Odysseus, whom the king had charged with the care of his house when he went away.

" Listen to me, men of Ithaca," he said, " your king Odysseus was gentle to all his people as a father. But you have forgotten his goodness to let these proud men prey upon his house. I do not blame them so much as you, for they are but a few and hazard their lives by what they are doing, while you sit by quietly and see it done."

But again the suitors were defiant and one of them shouted that Telemachus might find a ship if he could, but they would not yield for any words of Mentor. " And even if Odysseus ever came home again to turn us out, he might find himself outnumbered and his wife would have no joy of his return."

Then they broke up the assembly and the suitors returned to the palace of the king.

But Telemachus went down to the sea-shore and dipped his hands in the salt sea-foam, and prayed to the Goddess:

" Hear me, O thou who camest yesterday to our

house! Thou badest me take ship and go in search
of my father, but the suitors will not let me do thy
bidding."

And in answer to his prayer, Athena came, this
time in the form of Mentor, the guardian of his house.

".Telemachus," she said, " you will not fail if you
are your father's son. Take no heed of these suitors:
let them go their own way to their doom. I will see
to the ship and your company and will sail with you
myself. You must go up to the palace and make
ready the corn and wine for your voyage, and I will
have the best ship in Ithaca waiting at the furthest
quay."

So he went to the palace, and when he entered
the hall, Antinous came up to him with a laugh and
took him by the hand: "Sit down, Telemachus," he
cried, " sit down, brave youth! Let us have no more
of this bickering, but eat and drink as before."

But he drew back his hand and answered, " Antinous, I can sit no longer and feast in your company.
While I was a child, you wasted my substance at
your will and destroyed my house: now I am a man,
and I have heard the story and will brook the evil
no more. If there is no help for me in Ithaca, I shall
find it in Pylos and my voyage will not be in vain."

And he strode past the tables and out of the hall,
and as he passed, one or another of the suitors would
turn with a mocking word:

" He means mischief, I think." " He is going to
fetch help from foreign lands." " Or do you think

he will bring home some drugs to poison our drink?"
"It would be sad, if he perished at sea, like his
father; we should have to divide up the wealth
among us."

But Telemachus went down to his father's store-
room, a lofty chamber where gold and bronze lay in
plenty, and chests full of clothing, and casks of olive
oil and of wine. Eurycleia, the old nurse, kept watch
over the treasure, and Telemachus found her there
and called her to him:

"Nurse, give me twelve jars of your sweet wine,
not the best of all that you keep for my father's return,
but the next to that, and put twenty measures of
barley in some good stout skins; for I have to set
off to Pylos and Sparta this very night and no one
must know it, not even my mother herself."

And the kind old woman wept aloud when she
heard it and begged him not to go: "We have lost
Odysseus; you are all that is left to us. As soon as
you go, they will plot to murder you and will divide
all this treasure among them."

Then he comforted her and told her that it was
the will of Heaven that he should go and he made
her swear not to tell his mother till eleven days were
past.

So she hastened to do his bidding, and he went
back and waited in the hall.

Meanwhile the Goddess had found a ship and a
crew, and when all was ready she took the shape of
Mentor and went up to the palace to let Telemachus

know.   And as she entered, a strange drowsiness
came over the princes, so that their cups fell out of
their hands and they were soon glad to return to
the city and sleep.   Then she called to Telemachus
to follow her and led the way to the harbour.   There
was the ship's company, ready to embark, and when
they had brought down the stores from the palace,
they took their places; and the Goddess sat down
at the helm, with the young prince by her side.   And
a fresh breeze came whistling from the west and
filled their sail and they sped along all night, over
the dark blue waters: and as they went, they poured
out offerings of wine to the Gods who live for ever,
and, chief of all, to Athena, that wise daughter of
Father Zeus, the Goddess with the clear grey eyes.

CHAPTER III

HOW TELEMACHUS CAME TO PYLOS

ALL night the ship ran on, and in the morning, just as the sun leapt up from the waves, they came in sight of sandy Pylos and the fortress where Nestor lived. He was on the beach with all his people, making a solemn sacrifice to Poseidon, lord of the sea. And when the ship touched land Athena spoke to Telemachus, and bade him go boldly to Nestor and ask about his father whom he had crossed the sea to find. So they stepped ashore, and all the company went up to greet them; and Nestor's son took them by the hand, and made them sit down beside his father on the soft fleeces they had strewn upon the sand, and gave them meat and wine. And when they were refreshed Nestor said to the others, " Now we may ask the strangers who they are." And with that he turned to the two:

" Strangers, where do you come from? And why do you wander over the broad highways of the sea? Is it for traffic, or for the plunder that pirates love? "

Then Telemachus took heart and said,

" Nestor, son of Neleus, noblest of the Greeks, I

will tell you what you ask. My home is in Ithaca, and I have come to search for tidings of my father, Odysseus the stedfast-hearted, who fought with you at Troy, I have heard, and sacked the town. He has never returned and we do not know if he is alive or dead. And now I entreat you, for my father's sake and the love he bore you, tell me what has happened to him and do not hide the truth to spare me."

Then the old warrior sighed and said, " Ah! my friend, how well your words bring back to me that war, and all we suffered there, and the noble men we lost, Ajax, and Achilles, and my own son, the best of warriors! And are you indeed the son of Odysseus? Yes, you are like him when you speak, more like him than I would have thought so young a man could be. He was my faithful friend, and we were always of one mind and gave the same counsel to the Greeks. But I sailed away in haste from Troy, and I have never seen him since and only know by hearsay what happened to the rest. You must have heard yourselves of Agamemnon's fate, how he was murdered on his return in his own palace by Aegisthus and the faithless queen. But his valiant son has avenged him now and slain the traitor and won great glory for himself. And you will be as valiant as he, and famous among men, I know, for you are strong and fair, and I pray that Pallas Athena may watch over you, she who was your father's friend."

But Telemachus answered sadly, " Alas! my lord,

your hopes are far too high. The Gods have never meant such happiness for me; and even if it was their will, they could not help me here."

But Athena rebuked him for his doubts: " How can you speak like that, Telemachus? The Gods are far away, but they can help and save. And I would rather wait and suffer and come home safe at last, than perish like Agamemnon on the very day of my return."

But Telemachus would not be comforted. Then Nestor said, Menelaus might be able to give him tidings, for he had wandered far and wide and seen many lands before he had come home to Sparta again. And he offered to give Telemachus a chariot and send him there next day. " But you must stay this night with me, for it shall never be said that your father's son slept in his ship under the open sky, while I or son of mine was here to welcome him."

Then Athena thanked the old king and said Telemachus would stay, but there was other work for her to do and she must leave them. And as she spoke she rose and flew away like a sea-bird, leaving them all amazed. Nestor was the first to speak: " That was the warrior maiden, the glorious child of Zeus. She came to be your guide, Telemachus, and you cannot prove weak or base if the Gods are near you in your youth."

Then he took the prince up to his palace, and made him rest there that night. And next morning he

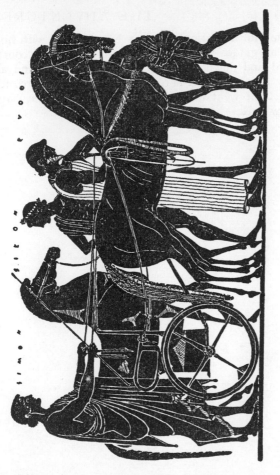

gave him a chariot and sent his own son with him for his guide. So they drove out of the echoing court-yard and down the steep hill to the plain, and all day long the sleek horses carried them forward, till the light went down in the west and all the ways grew dark.

CHAPTER IV

HOW TELEMACHUS WAS ENTERTAINED AT SPARTA

AT last they came to the hollow vale of Sparta and to the palace of Menelaus, the fair-haired king. There was a great banquet on foot in his hall, and all his neighbours and kinsmen were assembled, for both his son and his daughter were to be married that day. And as the company sat feasting and listening to the minstrel's song, news came that two strangers were at the gate. " Bring them in to feast with us," said the king. " No stranger shall go empty from our doors, for we ourselves have eaten the bread of strangers in other lands."

So the attendants brought Telemachus and the son of Nestor into the house; and they bathed themselves, and new clothes were given to them, and then they were led to the banqueting-hall. Seats were placed for them at the king's side, and Menelaus said to them, " Sit down and welcome to our feast. When you have eaten and drunk you shall tell us who you are; but I can see that you come of kingly stock."

So they sat down at the board, and as they feasted

they looked round them and wondered at the splendour of the hall: for the whole palace shone like the moon. And presently Telemachus said in a low voice to the son of Nestor, " Look, my friend, at the beauty of this house, how it glitters with bronze and silver and ivory and gold. It dazzles me to look at it. I think the palace of Zeus in heaven must shine like this."

" No, my son," said Menelaus; for he had heard what was said. "No palace upon earth can compare with the dwellings of the Immortals. Men may call me wealthy, it is true: and yet I would give the best part of my wealth to have those heroes back who fell upon the plains round Troy. Often as I sit here I think of them all until I weep: but the man I grieve for most is the godlike Odysseus. He was ever the first of the Greeks in all adventures; but ill-fortune befell him, and now we know not whether he is alive or dead."

When Telemachus heard his father's name he could not keep back his tears, and he hid his face in his cloak; and Menelaus watched him, and wondered if he should ask him who he was. But at that moment Helen came from her chamber, fair as the Goddess Artemis. Her maidservants set her chair ready, and brought her a golden distaff and a silver basket full of purple yarn. So she took her seat and then she said to her husband, " Who are these guests, Menelaus? One of them is strangely like the noble Odysseus. Surely it must be Telemachus, the little son whom he left behind when he sailed for Troy."

"Yes," answered Menelaus, "I see myself how

like he is. And even now, when I spoke of Odysseus, he hid his face and wept."

Then the son of Nestor said, "Noble Menelaus, this is indeed the son of Odysseus; and Nestor my father sent me to guide him to your palace, for he hoped that he might find help or comfort here. His father has never returned, and he has no one in Ithaca to take his part."

At that Menelaus welcomed Telemachus afresh for his father's sake, and told him how valiantly Odysseus had fought in his cause at Troy and how dearly he loved him in return. And as he thought upon old days he shed tears, and Helen wept with him, and the son of Nestor wept too, for he remembered his valiant brother who had died at Troy. But Helen thought how she might comfort them, and she mingled in the wine a magic drug. It was brought from Egypt, the land where strange herbs grow, and it could soothe all pain and bring forgetfulness of every grief: the man who should once taste it would shed no tear that day, not though he saw his own brother slain with the sword before his face. This drug she mingled in the wine and bade the steward bear it round, and then she spoke of Odysseus and his wisdom and courage.

" I remember that time in the war," she said, " when he came into Troy alone. What a deed that was! He disguised himself as a beggar and so made his way into the enemy's town, and no one guessed who he was but I. I questioned him, but he turned my questions aside, till I took him into my own chamber and swore that I would not betray him; and then he told me the purposes of the Greeks, and he went back to the camp in safety with his news. And I rejoiced, for my heart had turned again to my own people, and I wept to think how I left my home and my husband, the noblest of men."

"Yes," said Menelaus, "and how he showed his wisdom when we lay in the wooden horse with the chosen band! The Trojans had brought it into the the city, and then you came and put your hand on it, and walked round it, calling us all by name. It seemed to each of us as if it were his own wife's voice, and we would have answered: but Odysseus made us hold our peace and so he saved our lives."

Thus they told tales of old adventures, until the time for rest was come.

Next morning Menelaus made Telemachus sit by his side, and asked what had brought him to Sparta; and when he had heard the story and what wrongs the suitors did, he cried out in fury, "Shame upon the dastards! They have made their bed in a lion's lair : but the lion will come back and he will not spare them. And now I will tell you all I know of the fate of Odysseus, as it was told to me by the wizard Proteus, the herdsman of Poseidon, who knows all the depths of the sea.

"As I was sailing home from Troy, my ship was windbound on a desert island off the coast of Egypt. The days went by and our store of food was nearly spent, and we went roaming along the shore in search of fish. At last one morning, as I was alone on the beach, a sea-nymph saw me and had pity on me, and rose from the heaving waters to give me counsel.

She said that she was the daughter of Proteus, and that her father could tell me how to escape, but I must take him prisoner first. Then she shewed me where he would come at noon to count over his flock of seals, and she told me how I might seize him; and when I seized him, she said he would turn into all manner of shapes, but I must hold him fast and in the end he would answer me.

"So I called three of my comrades, and we scooped out holes in the sand and lay down, and the nymph brought skins of seals and threw them over us. There we waited while the seals came up from the salt water and settled themselves upon the beach. At noontide Proteus rose from the waves, and went along the line and counted all his flock, and then lay down to rest. And as soon as he was asleep up we sprang and seized him. Then he turned himself into all manner of shapes, into a lion and a serpent and a stream of water and a tall branching tree; but we held him fast all the while, as the sea-nymph had bidden us, and in the end he took his own form again and told me all I asked him. First he told me that the Gods were angry with me, but I might turn away their wrath by sacrifice and so come safely home at last. And then he told me the fate of the Greek heroes who had fought at Troy, how some had returned safely and some were lost at sea, and how my own brother Agamemnon was slain by treachery when he had just set foot on land. Last of all he said, 'And one of the heroes is yet living on an island in the far-off seas: it is Odysseus, king of Ithaca. I saw him prisoner in the cave of the nymph Calypso: his ships are wrecked and his comrades lost, and big tears fall from his eyes as he thinks upon the home he cannot reach.'

"That was the tale which I heard from the old wizard of the sea; and after that I offered sacrifice to the Gods, and they brought me to Sparta in safety."

Thus Menelaus and Helen entertained Telemachus in their halls. Meanwhile in Ithaca the suitors heard how he had taken a ship and gone to Pylos. "We shall have trouble with this youth," said Antinous, "unless we rid ourselves of him in time. Give me a ship and twenty men, and I will lie in wait for him off Samos in the strait and put an end to his journeys." So they manned a ship and lay in wait off Samos to take Telemachus on his way home.

But Medon the herald heard their plot, and he went and told Penelope. She had not yet learned that her son was gone from home; and she was broken-hearted at the news, and sat on the ground and wept among her women, and blamed them all for hiding from her what had happened. Then the old nurse Eurycleia said, " Slay me if you will, my child, but I will tell you the truth. I knew that he was gone, but he made me swear that I would not tell you till eleven days were past. Pray to Pallas Athena, the child of Zeus, for it can never be

*B

the will of heaven to root out utterly this ancient house."

So Penelope dried her tears and went apart with her women and prayed to Athena: "Hear me, warrior maiden, child of Zeus! Call to mind how Odysseus honoured thee, and deliver my son from the enemies who lie in wait for him." And all day long she lay alone in her upper chamber, thinking of her son and tasting neither food nor drink, while below in the hall the suitors revelled and boasted how they would win her for themselves.

But in the dead of night a vision came to Penelope through the gate of dreams. She thought that her sister, whose home was far away, stood beside her bed and said to her, "Why is your heart so sore, Penelope? Your son will return to you: the Gods have not abandoned him."

And Penelope said in her dream, "Sister, it is long since I have seen you. Are you come to comfort me in my troubles? I have much need of comfort. I have lost my lion-hearted husband, whose fame was spread abroad through all the land of Greece; and now my son is gone over seas and I tremble at what may happen to him, for there are many foes that seek his life."

And the dim phantom answered, "Have no fear for your son. Pallas Athena will be his friend and guide. She has charged me to tell you this, for she has pity on your grief."

Then Penelope said again, "If you are in truth

an Immortal or have had speech with Immortals, tell me of my lord. Does he still see the light of the sun?"

And the dim phantom answered, "Of him I cannot tell you: question me no more."

Then the dream vanished into the air, and the queen awoke and her heart was comforted.

CHAPTER V

HOW ODYSSEUS CAME TO THE LAND OF THE SEA-KINGS

BUT next morning when the Gods were sitting in council and Zeus among them, Athena spoke of Odysseus again, for she never forgot how he suffered in Calypso's cave. " O, Father Zeus," she said, " why should any man be a just and righteous king? For see how all his people have forgotten Odysseus, who was gentle as a father, and now the suitors are plotting to kill his son, as he comes back from Pylos and Sparta."

And the lord of the thunder answered, " My child, have you not planned yourself that in the end Odysseus shall take vengeance on all his enemies? But see that Telemachus returns home safely and that the suitors make their voyage in vain." And he said to Hermes, " My son, go to Calypso, the nymph with the beautiful hair, and tell her that Odysseus must leave her. He must build a raft and set sail, and after twenty days he will reach the land of the Sea-kings, who will load him with gifts and send him on his way. And so he shall see his home and his kindred again."

Then Hermes took his magic wand and bound his golden sandals on his feet and leapt down from sky to sea, and flew over the depths like a cormorant, as it chases the fish through the waves and dips its feathers in the foam. And when he reached the far-off island, he went up to the lofty cave and found Calypso alone within, singing sweetly as she wove at her loom with a golden shuttle. A great fire was burning on the hearth and the scent of the burning cedar-wood was wafted through the island. Round the cave was a grove of stately trees, alders and poplars and sweet-smelling cypresses, where the birds came to roost at night, falcons and owls and sea-mews who are busy in the waves. And over the mouth of the cave a garden vine was growing, thick with clustering grapes, and there were four springs beside it, and four clear streams that ran through flowering meadows of parsley and violet. It was all so beautiful that even a God might stand and wonder. At last he entered and the Goddess knew him and made him sit down on a shining seat and gave him ambrosia and nectar, the food of the Immortals, and said, " Tell me your errand, Hermes, for it is not your wont to visit here."

Then he told her how Zeus had taken pity on Odysseus who had been kept so many years from his home by war and tempest, and bade her send him on his way as quickly as she could. The Goddess shuddered when she heard his message and said, " Cruel Gods, you are jealous of my friend and guest! I saved him when he was left alone, clinging to the wreck of his ship when Zeus had struck it with his thunderbolt and shattered it in mid-sea. But if it is the will of Zeus that he depart, I will not hinder him; I cannot send him myself, for I have no ships nor men; but I will tell him all you say."

And Hermes said, "Do so at once, lest Zeus be angry."

So he departed, and Calypso went out to seek Odysseus on the shore. And she found him sitting there and weeping as he looked across the barren sea; for so he sat day by day. "Unhappy man," she said, "do not sorrow any more, for I have come to let you go, and I will give you all the help I can. Come, build a raft and make it strong enough for the sea, and I will give you bread and wine and water to last you on your journey, and a fair wind to follow in your wake and bring you safely home, if such is the will of the Gods, who are wiser and stronger than I."

But Odysseus could not believe her words, and he was not satisfied until she swore a solemn oath by earth and heaven and the world below that she did not mean to work him harm.

Then they went back to the cave and feasted and talked till evening. Nectar and ambrosia were set before Calypso, but Odysseus ate the common fare of mortal men.

At last the Goddess said, "Odysseus, if you are

resolved to return to Ithaca and the wife you love,
I wish you well. Yet if you knew what suffering you
have in store before you see her, you would remain
with me, I think, and be immortal. I am a Goddess,
and can I be less beautiful or less noble than your
mortal wife? "

And he replied, " Goddess and queen, I know full
well Penelope cannot compare with you in form or
stature. She will grow old and die. Yet I long day
and night to see her, and would endure another
shipwreck and untold sorrows to be at home again.
I can bear them as I have borne the rest."

When morning came Calypso gave him a great
bronze axe and a hatchet; and they went out to
the wood, and there the Goddess showed him where
the tall trees grew, and left him to his work. He soon
felled a score, and made the timbers straight and
smooth and jointed them together, and fitted the raft
with a gunwale, and a rudder and a mast. In four
days he finished and launched it, and made his sails.
And on the fifth he stored it well with food and water
and wine that the Goddess gave him, and then set
sail with a joyful heart. For seventeen days and
nights he never slept, but steered straight on, watching the Pleiades and Boötes, and always keeping on
his left hand, as the Goddess had bidden him, those
great stars that some men call the Bear and some
the Wain. And on the eighteenth day he sighted
the shadowy hills of the Sea-kings' land, like a
shield upon the misty waters.

But Poseidon was on his way back from Ethiopia, riding in his chariot over the waves, and he saw Odysseus from afar, and anger filled him at the sight. " So! " he cried, " the Gods have changed their plans while I was away from Olympus. And Odysseus is close to the shore where he will be safe from me. But he shall have more trouble first." Then, grasping his trident, he gathered the clouds and roused the winds and brought down night from heaven.

Then the brave heart of Odysseus sank within him, and he recalled the warning of the nymph, aye, and envied the Greeks who died at Troy. " Would that I had died that day when the Trojans overwhelmed me with their spears! Then I should have died with glory, but this is a piteous end."

And, as he spoke, a huge wave fell upon him and swept him from the raft, and he was overwhelmed by the surging waters. His garments weighed him down, but at last he rose, and even in this peril remembered the raft, and clutched at it, and dragged himself upon it. And the waves bore it hither and thither, and the four winds blew upon it all together, tossing it to and fro, like a tuft of thistledown.

Then Odysseus would have perished at last, had not one of the sea-nymphs, Ino the slender-footed, who had been a woman once, taken pity on him in his need. She rose from the gulfs like a seabird, and perched upon the raft. " Unhappy man," she said, " why does Poseidon hate you so? But he shall not destroy you after all. Strip off your garments, and leave your raft to drift before the winds. Then fasten this magic veil beneath your breast, and swim to land. But when you have touched the shore, loose it and throw it far back into the sea, and as you throw it, turn away your eyes."

Then she gave him the veil, and dived back into the surge like a sea-gull, and the dark waters hid her from his sight. Then Odysseus thought to himself, " Is this another snare of the Immortals, to bid me quit my raft? I will not leave it yet, for the land is a long way off. No, so long as the timbers hold together, I will remain on the raft, whatever I may suffer. But when the waves have broken it to pieces, then I will trust to swimming."

But while he was thinking, a great crested wave came down upon him, and scattered the timbers of the raft, as the wind scatters a heap of chaff, and Odysseus was left astride on a single beam. Then he stripped off the garments which Calypso had given him, and wound the sea-nymph's veil beneath his breast, and plunged into the sea. And when Poseidon saw him swimming, he shook his head and said, " Drift on and suffer till you reach land again, and even there you will suffer your fill."

With that he lashed his steeds and turned away, but Athena bound up all the winds except the north, which blew strong and carried Odysseus towards the Sea-kings' land. Two nights and two days he struggled forward, and on the third day when the bright-haired dawn was in the sky the wind fell, and from the top of a rising wave he saw the coast. The sight made him as glad as children are who see their father well again after a long and wasting sickness. But when he had swum near enough to hear the thunder of the breakers, and saw that there was no harbour and no shelter and only cliffs and jagged reefs, then at last his knees were loosened and his heart sank within him and he cried, " Can it be that I have struggled hither against all hope and yet there is no place to land ? If I go on, the waves will dash me on the rocks, and the cliffs are so sheer and the water so deep that I can gain no foothold. If I swim along the coast to find some shelter, the winds may bear me out again to sea, or Poseidon may send some monster to devour me, and there are many such."

At that moment a billow swept him towards the cliffs, and there all his bones would have been broken, had he not thought of clutching at a rock and clinging to it with both hands till the wave had passed. But as it ebbed back again, it dragged him away with it and stripped his hands of skin, as a cuttlefish is dragged from its hole with pebbles clinging to its suckers. But he saved himself by turning and swimming along the shore outside the breakers, till he came to the mouth of a river free from rocks and sheltered from the wind.

He felt the river flowing and prayed to the River-God : " Hear me, O King, whoever thou art, for I come as a wanderer flying from Poseidon's wrath. Take pity on me, I pray thee." Then the river stayed his stream and smoothed his waters, and so Odysseus made his way to land. And then his knees gave way beneath him, and his strong arms dropped at his sides, and he fell senseless on the shore. There for a time he lay swooning, while the salt water streamed from his mouth and nostrils. But when at last he came to himself, he loosed the magic veil and threw it back into the water. And a great wave came and bore it out to sea, where Ino rose and caught it in her hands. But Odysseus sank down among the rushes by the river-bank, and kissed the kindly earth.

Then he thought to himself, "What shall I do now? If I spend the night by the river, the dew and the frost may kill me, and the morning-breeze blows cold. But if I go up the hillside and fall asleep in the wood, the savage beasts may devour me."

At last he found a thicket near the river, and in it two bushes so closely grown together that neither wind nor rain nor sun could pierce them. He crept under the branches, and heaped up a couch of fallen leaves. There was abundance of them there, enough to cover him as well as to lie upon, and he lay down among them, and covered himself up as a country-man who lives in a lonely place will cover up his fire under the ashes to keep it alive. And Athena shed sleep on his eyes to take away his weariness and pain.

CHAPTER VI

HOW ODYSSEUS MET THE PRINCESS NAUSICAA

So there the stout-hearted Odysseus lay and slept, worn-out with all his toil. But meanwhile Athena went to the Sea-kings' city, up to the palace of their ruler, the wise Alcinous, and into the beautiful chamber where his daughter lay asleep, the young princess Nausicaa, fair as the Immortals. On either side of the threshold two maidens were sleeping, as lovely as the Graces, and the glittering doors were shut. But the Goddess floated through them like a breath of wind, up to the head of the couch, and spoke to Nausicaa in a dream. She seemed to her one of her dear companions, the daughter of Dymas, the sailor.

"How heedless you are, Nausicaa!" so the vision said. "You let all your fine clothing lie uncared for, and your marriage-day must be close at hand, when you ought to have beautiful robes for yourself and for your maidens, if you wish your friends to praise you and your father and mother to be glad. Let us take the clothes down to the river and wash them, early to-morrow morning. I will help you in the work, for we must get ready as quickly as we can; the best men among your people are suitors for you already.

And ask the king your father to give you a pair of mules and a car, for the river is a long way off."

Then Athena went back to Olympus, the peaceful home of the Gods. No winds blow there, so men say, and no rain falls, and the snow never comes near it, but the whole sky is calm and cloudless and all the air is full of light.

So the night passed away, and the young Dawn appeared on her glorious throne in the sky and awakened the princess. She was full of wonder at the dream, and went through the house to tell her parents, and found them in the hall. Her mother was sitting by the hearth among her maidens spinning her sea-blue yarn, and she met her father at the door, on his way to the council of his lords. Nausicaa ran up to him and said:

" Father dear, we have so much fine linen lying soiled in the house,—could you not lend me a pair of mules and a car, and I will take it all down to the river and wash it? You must have clean robes to wear yourself when you sit at the council among the chiefs, and you have five sons at home, three of them young and bachelors, and they always want fresh linen for the dances, and I must think of it all."

She was too shy to speak about her marriage to her father; but he understood, and answered, " You may have the mules, my child, and anything you wish."

So the princess brought out the bright garments and put them on the car; and her mother packed a store of dainties in a basket, and gave her a goatskin full of wine, and olive-oil in a golden flask. Then Nausicaa mounted the car, and her maidens went with her, and she took the whip and the glistening reins, and started the mules, and they clattered off at once and carried her willingly all the way.

At last they came to the flowing river, and there they stopped and unyoked the mules, and sent them to feed on the sweet clover that grew along the banks; and they lifted out the clothes and laid them in the trenches, and trod them in the dark water, vying with one another in the work. And when they had finished, they spread them out on the beach to dry in the sun, just where the sea had washed the pebbles clean. Then they bathed and anointed themselves, and took their meal at the riverside, and afterwards they threw aside their veils and played at ball, and white-armed Nausicaa led the song. And she looked like Artemis the huntress on the hillside among the mountain nymphs, taller by the head and fairer and statelier than them all.

At last it was time to go home, and they harnessed the mules and folded up the clothes. But now Athena planned that Odysseus should awake and see the maiden. Just then the princess had the ball, and she threw it to one of the girls, but it missed her and dropped into the eddying river, and they cried out as they saw it go. The cry woke Odysseus, and he sprang up in wonder.

"Where am I?" he asked himself. "What country

can this be? I hear the sound of women's voices. Are they mortals, or nymphs of the meadows and the stream? I will go and see."

Then **he** broke off a leafy bough **to** cover his loins,

and went out from his shelter in the wood to meet the fair-haired maidens, all rough and naked as he was,—his need was so great,—like a mountain-lion stalking through wind and rain after the forest deer. But they were terrified when they saw him, covered

with the salt sea-brine, and they ran away from him
to the end of the curving beach. Only the daughter
of Alcinous stood where she was, and waited for him,
face to face without trembling, for Athena gave her
courage. Then Odysseus spoke to her gently, and he
knew what was best to say.

"Maiden," he said, "whoever you are, I need
your help. Surely you must be Artemis the huntress, if you are one of the Immortals. Or are you
a mortal maiden? Then how happy must your
father be and your mother and your brothers when
they watch you in the dance! Only once have
I seen a thing so fair, long ago in Delos, a young
sapling palm-tree, straight and tall and wonderful,
that grew by Apollo's temple. Princess, I have
suffered much. I have been wandering over the
dark sea for twenty days and nights, tossed to and
fro by wave and storm, and at last I have landed
here. But I am a stranger, and do not know the
people of the land. You are the first I have met
and I ask you to help me. In kindness show me the
way to the city and give me clothing, some wrapper
you have used for the linen. So may the Gods grant
you your heart's desire, a worthy husband and love
and unity in your home. For no power in the world
is stronger than the husband and wife who are one
at heart; their enemies cannot hurt them and their
friends rejoice, but they know their own joy best
themselves."

And Nausicaa said to him, "Stranger, it is Zeus

who gives us everything, sorrow and happiness alike. You must bear what he has sent you, and you seem to me brave and wise. And now that you have come to us and asked me for help, you shall have everything you need. This is the land of the Sea-kings, and I am the daughter of their ruler, the great-hearted Alcinous."

Then she called to her maidens, "Come back to me, girls; why do you run away? This man is no enemy, but a shipwrecked wanderer, and we must treat him kindly. All strangers and suppliants are sent to us by Zeus. Give him food and drink and let him bathe in the river, somewhere out of the wind."

So they took Odysseus to a sheltered place, and gave him a doublet and a cloak, and soft olive-oil in a golden flask, and showed him where to bathe. And he washed away the salt sea-brine from his limbs, and the scurf of salt from his hair, and anointed himself and put on the garments, and his long curls fell clustering round his shoulders, and Athena gave him grace and stateliness. Then he came back to the maiden and sat down on the beach, and the princess looked at him and said to her women:

"The Gods themselves have sent this stranger here. At first I thought him ill-favoured, but now he looks like one of the Immortals, the lords of heaven and earth. Oh that such a hero would stay with us and be my husband! Go now, give him food and drink."

But when Odysseus had eaten and drunk his fill, another thought came into Nausicaa's mind. She folded away the linen and mounted the car, and then called Odysseus to her side and said:

"Come, stranger, let us gō to the city, and I will send you to my father's house. But you must do as I tell you, and you will understand, I think, why it is best. So long as we go through the meadows, follow close behind me with my maidens, and I will lead the way. But when we come near the city,—

you will see a high wall round it and a noble harbour
on either side with a narrow neck of land between,
and the ships drawn up along the road, each one in
its own station. Close by is the public square, and
Poseidon's sacred place, and the shipyards where
they make the sails and ropes and shave the oars.
Now there are insolent men among our folk, and
some of them might say, 'Who is the tall kingly
stranger with Nausicaa? Some wanderer from a
distant land, or a God perhaps, come down from
heaven at her prayer! It is well that she has found
a foreign husband for herself, since she scorns the
noble Sea-kings who make their suit to her!' Thus
they will reproach me, and I should blame it myself
in another maid. So listen to my plan. You will
find a grove of Athena on the way, tall poplars and
a running spring and a meadow close beside them.
Sit there, and wait until we are home again. And
when you think it time, follow us to the city and ask
for my father's house: it is easy to find, for none of
the rest are like it. Go straight up through the hall
to my mother: she will be sitting by the hearth in
the firelight, her chair against a pillar, spinning her
wonderful sea-blue yarn, and her maidens sit behind
her. My father's throne is next to hers: there he
sits and drinks his wine, like one of the Immortals.
But go past him and put your hands on my mother's
knees, for you will soon see your home again if you
can win her favour."

Then Nausicaa lifted the whip and the mules

started for home. And as the sun set they came to the sacred grove of Athena. There Odysseus sat down and waited, and he prayed to the Goddess that the Sea-kings might pity him and give him help, and she heard his prayer.

CHAPTER VII

HOW ODYSSEUS WAS RECEIVED IN THE PALACE OF ALCINOUS

MEANWHILE the princess had reached her father's house, and the young princes her brothers met her at the porch and unyoked her mules and carried the garments into the house. And she went to her own bright chamber where her old nurse lit the fire and prepared her supper.

Just then Odysseus started for the city, and Athena spread a mist about him lest any of the proud Sea-kings should be aware of him and mock him and ask him who he was. But when he entered the city, she met him herself in the form of a maiden carrying a pitcher; and as she stopped before him, he said, "My child, can you tell me where King Alcinous lives, for I am a stranger in this place?"

And she replied, "Follow me, sir, and I will show you his house; for it is near where my own father lives. But do not speak to anyone by the way, for my countrymen are not too fond of strangers. They put their trust in their ships and sail everywhere over the great waters, for Poseidon has made them kings of the sea." So saying she led the way quickly, and Odysseus followed. And as he went along, he could see the harbours and ships and long high walls and public squares, and marvelled at it all, but no one could see him for he was covered by the mist.

When they reached the palace of the king, Athena said, " This is the house, father, which you bade me show you. Kings are sitting there at the feast; but enter boldly, for a brave heart fares best. You will find the queen first: her name is Arete, and she is honoured by her husband and her children and her people as no other woman in the world is honoured. She is wise, too, and can settle men's quarrels when she will. If you can only win her favour, you may hope to see your friends and your native land again."

And then the Goddess went back over the sea to Marathon and her good house at Athens, while Odysseus entered the palace of Alcinous and wondered at what he saw. For the whole house shone like the sun or the moon. The walls were all of bronze and the doors of gold. The doorposts and the lintel were silver, and on each side stood dogs of gold and silver which never grew old nor died. Inside along the walls were rows of seats, spread with fine coverlets woven by the women, where the Sea-kings sat at the banquet. And boys of gold stood round the hall, with torches in their hands to give them light. There were fifty maidservants in the house, some to grind the corn and some to spin and some to weave; and they weave their cloth as skilfully as the men can sail their ships. Before the gate was a garden with pear-trees and pomegranates and olives in their bloom, and bright apples and sweet figs, which grew and ripened all the year round. And there was a fruitful vineyard, where some of the grapes were just turning colour and some were being dried and others pressed, and flower-beds of every colour always in blossom, and two fountains, one that watered the garden and one at the courtyard-gate for the towns-folk.

Odysseus stood awhile outside, and gazed at it all in wonder. Then he crossed the threshold and walked straight through the hall to the place where the king and queen were sitting. The princes were all drinking at the tables, but no one saw him as he passed because of the mist about him. But when he came to the queen's throne the mist suddenly rolled away, and all the company saw him and gazed in silence and amazement. Then he knelt down and put his hand on her knees and made his prayer : " Lady and Queen, take pity on me, unhappy wanderer that I am, and send me to my far-off home; and I will pray the Gods that they may give happiness and worthy children and every honour to you and to your husband and to these noble guests."

Then he sat down like a suppliant on the hearth, and still they all gazed in silence, till at last one old lord, wiser and readier than the rest, spoke out: " Alcinous, we wait upon your word; but surely it is not seemly that a guest should sit among the ashes in the suppliant's place. Lead him, I pray you, to an honourable seat and let him have food and drink, while we will fill our cups and drink in his honour."

Then Alcinous took Odysseus by the hand and raised him from the ashes and put him by his side in his own son's place. And the servants washed his hands and spread a table with good things and set it by him. And when the feast was over, Alcinous said, " My lords, I have a word to say before you go. To-morrow morning we will meet in council to receive this stranger and provide for his return, for if he sails in a ship of ours no harm can happen to him on his way. But if he is an Immortal, the Gods are dealing with us as they have never dealt before. They have ever met us as neighbours, openly and face to face; for we are near of kin to them, like the Cyclops and the Giants."

Then Odysseus said, " I am no Immortal, Alcinous, but the most afflicted of all mortal men, and I could tell a long tale of the sufferings that the Gods have given me to bear. But now, I pray you, let me forget my troubles, and in the morning make haste to send me on my way, for all I now desire in life is to see my people and my home again."

The nobles promised that it should be so, and then they went home for the night; and Odysseus was left in the hall with Alcinous and the queen, while the maidens cleared away the feast.

Now Arete had noticed his cloak and doublet, for she and her women had made them. So she said, ' Stranger, I must first ask you this. Whence have

C 10

you come? And who has given you these garments? Did you not say that you were a wanderer from over seas?"

And Odysseus answered, "My story, lady, is long and sad, but I will tell you this. I have come from a far-off island where a Goddess lives, Calypso of the beautiful tresses. A storm drove me there and destroyed my ship and all my company, and the Goddess took me in and fed and cherished me and promised to make me live for ever and never grow old. But I always longed to depart, and at last, after seven years, she let me go. So I built a good stout raft and stored it with food and clothing that she gave me, and sailed away before a soft and favouring breeze. But on the eighteenth day, just as I caught sight of your shadowy hills above the sea, Poseidon raised the winds against me and I was wrecked once more. Naked and scarce alive I swam to shore and found a resting-place near the river's mouth, where I slept among the bushes with leaves for my covering. Next day at sundown I woke and found your daughter and her companions playing on the shore, and made my prayer to her. And she showed a wisdom that was strange in one so young and gave me food and drink and the garments that you see."

But Alcinous said, "Stranger, in one thing my daughter did amiss. She should have brought you to the house in her train, when you had asked her favour."

Then Odysseus answered, " Blame her not, my lord; she would have brought me had I wished. But I feared the sight might anger you, and so remained behind; we men are quick to take offence."

" Sir," replied Alcinous, " I am not so quick at that. Nay, I would gladly have such a man as you are to be my son-in-law, and would give you house and wealth to stay with us. But no one shall keep you here against your will. So, when to-morrow comes, you shall have your escort who will row you quickly over the sea as you lie asleep. However far you may wish to go, they can take you there and return in one day, and not be weary. For we have the best sailors and the most wonderful ships in the world."

Meanwhile Arete had bidden her maidens make a bed in the corridor with soft purple blankets and a thick covering over all. Hither they led Odysseus, torch in hand, and he lay down gladly and fell asleep.

And Alcinous and his wife went to their own chamber behind the hall.

CHAPTER VIII

HOW ODYSSEUS CONTENDED WITH THE SEA-KINGS IN THEIR GAMES

NEXT morning the king took Odysseus with him to the market-place close beside the harbour, and they sat down there on the seats of polished stone, while Athena in the herald's shape went through the town, bidding the people come and see the godlike stranger, so that they thronged the square. Then Alcinous rose in the midst and said, " Princes and friends, this stranger—I do not know his name—has come to my house and asked me for a guide to take him home. Let us do as we have always done, and help him on his way."

Then he told them to prepare a ship and choose fifty of the best sailors for her crew, and come to the palace afterwards to feast in honour of his guest. So they made the ship ready, and then sat down to the feast, and their minstrel came into the hall. A herald led him by the hand, for he was blind. But the Gods had given him joy as well as sorrow: they had taken his sight from him, but they gave him the gift of song. And he sang of the heroes of Troy and the siege, till Odysseus wept as he listened. But

he was ashamed for the kings to see his tears and
hid his face in his cloak, so that none of them noticed
but Alcinous, who sat beside him. And when he saw
it he broke up the banquet, and told the princes
they ought to show the stranger what skill they had
in every kind of game. So they ran races and threw
quoits and boxed and wrestled and leapt, until at
last one of them said to the others:

" Come, let us ask our guest if there is anything
he can do. He looks a stalwart man, broad-shouldered
and stout-limbed, and young and strong enough,
though somewhat broken with all the hardships he
has borne."

So they challenged Odysseus to try his hand; but
he only said, " I have more taste for grieving than
for games. I have toiled and suffered for years, and
I sit here now, longing for my return, asking your
king and all your people to send me on my way."

At that one of them, whose name was Euryalus,
sneered openly, and said, " No, stranger, I should
not think that you would care for games. You have
spent your time, I should say, on board a merchant-
man, and know more about cargoes and profits and
traders' tricks. No, you have not the look of an
athlete."

But Odysseus glanced at him sternly under his
deep brows and said, " Sir, there is little grace in
such a speech. The Gods, I see, will never give all
their favours to one man. They have given you
beauty in full measure, but a scanty store of sense.

Now your taunts have stung me, for I am not the weakling you say, but may count myself, I think, as good as any man while I have the strength of my prime. I am stiff with toils and sufferings now, but I will show you what I can do."

Then, without throwing his cloak aside, he sprang up and lifted a great quoit that lay beside him, far heavier and larger than any the Sea-kings threw. He poised it and hurled, and all the sailors shrank aside as the stone whizzed past and fell far beyond the rest, so that Odysseus smiled for pleasure and said with a light heart:

" Match that throw, my friends! Or challenge me to run or box or wrestle, and I will not draw back. And I can handle a bow at need. I have shot with the best archers living, and only found one man who could surpass me."

Odysseus paused, but all the Sea-kings were silent, and only Alcinous said, " Friend, no man of sense could despise your strength and skill. Indeed, we are not the best of boxers or wrestlers, but we are nimble-footed, and our ships are swifter than thought, and we love the banquet and the lute and the dance and changes of raiment and warm baths and sleep. And now my people shall dance for you, and you shall tell your wife and children at home what wonderful dancers they are."

With that he called two of his sons, and they came forward at his bidding; and the heralds made a ring and the minstrel played for them, and they danced and leapt and threw a crimson ball to one another, backwards and forwards, and up and down, catching it in the air, till Odysseus wondered at the twinkling of their feet, and turned to the king, praising their skill to his heart's content.

Then Alcinous asked each of the princes to bring a present for their guest, a bright cloak and a doublet and a talent of solid gold, and he said that Euryalus should make a special gift and ask the stranger's pardon for his lack of courtesy. Euryalus was ready enough to obey, and brought a great bronze sword with a silver hilt and a scabbard of carved ivory and gave it to Odysseus, saying:

" Sir, you are a welcome guest. Forgive me if my words were rough and let the wind blow them all away. And I wish you a safe return to your country and your wife, for you have been long away and have had many a trial to bear."

Then Odysseus said, " And you, friend, I wish you well. May all good fortune follow you, and may you never need this blade that you have given me in your courtesy."

So saying he took the sword and slung it over his shoulder. By this time the sun had set, and Alcinous led the way home to the palace, and Odysseus went to his chamber and bathed and came down again to the hall where the kings were sitting at their wine. There Nausicaa stood in her beauty beside the door, and she looked at him in wonder and said:

" Farewell, stranger! Remember me sometimes

even when you are home again in your native land, for I was the first to help you."

And Odysseus answered, " Princess, may it be as you say! May I see my home once more! I will think of you there, and you will always seem like one of the Gods to me, for it was you that brought me back to life."

Then he went on into the hall and sat down by the king. And he asked the minstrel to sing to them again, a song about the wooden horse and the cunning plan by which Odysseus took the citadel of Troy. But when the song began, his tears gathered and fell, so that Alcinous noticed it again and broke off the song, crying,

" Hush! Let the minstrel cease! Perhaps his song does not please all our company; ever since he began our guest has wept for sorrow. So let us have no more, and then we can all be glad, guest and host alike."

With that he turned to Odysseus: " Hide your secret no longer; surely you may tell it now. Tell us your name, and your country, and where you have wandered, and the cities and men you have seen, and why you wept when you heard of the Greeks and their fate at Troy. Has one of your kindred perished there? Or a true comrade whom you loved? A loyal and trusted friend is as near to us as a brother."

CHAPTER IX

HOW ODYSSEUS ESCAPED FROM THE CYCLOPS

THEN Odysseus answered:

" King Alcinous, it is good to see a whole people met together like this in the palace-hall, taking their pleasure at the feast, while the minstrel sings a glorious song for them to hear. This is a pure delight; but there is little joy in the story you ask me for; in sorrow it must begin and in sorrow end.

" I am Odysseus, the son of Laertes, and the fame of my wisdom has gone through all the world. My home is the island Ithaca: it rises far-off in the western sea, a rugged land, but a good nurse of heroes, and no place could be so dear in my sight. My father and mother lived there, and there I was born. I longed for it even when Calypso, the fairest of nymphs, kept me in her hollow caves, even when Circe, the enchantress, tried to win my heart. But now I will tell you what you ask: the tale of my wanderings and my sufferings on the way home from Troy.

" From the first we had trouble enough by sea and land; but we reached the Cape of Malea at last and had almost rounded it, when the North wind

*C

swept down on us and drove us out of our course. Nine days we drifted before the gale, but on the tenth we came to the land of the lotus-eaters, a people who live on flowers. We went on shore and took our mid-day meal by the beach, and I sent three of my comrades to find out what sort of men lived there. The lotus-eaters were kind to them, and gave them lotus to taste. It was sweet as honey, and all who took it forgot their country and longed to stay there and eat it for ever. But I forced them back to the ships, though they wept to come away, and I bound them under the benches and hurried the rest on board; and so we put to sea.

"Then we sailed on sadly till we came to the land of the Cyclops, a savage and lawless race. They never plough and they sow no seed; but wheat and barley and fruitful vines grow wild in their land. They dwell alone in caves among the mountains, and each one lays down the law himself for his wife and children, and cares for no one else. At the mouth of the bay where they live there is a wooded island. It is a lonely place, full of wild goats, with no sign of man to frighten them away. No shepherds come there and no hunters, for the Cyclops have no ships to cross the sea and no shipwrights to build them. Yet it is a fertile land and men might settle there; it would bear all kinds of fruit in their season; there are rich water-meadows by the sea, and vines that never fail, and level fields for ploughing, and a harbour where ships could lie without rope or anchor, and at the head of it a cave with a spring of sparkling water and poplars growing all around. We ran in there on a dark night, and some God must have been our guide; for there was no moon and the mist lay thick over the sea, so that none of us saw the land nor the long rollers on the beach, until the ships were aground.

" We lay down on the shore and slept within sound of the sea till dawn, and then we took our bows and long hunting-spears, and followed the mountain-goats, and soon brought down game enough, nine for each of the twelve ships that sailed with me and ten for my own crew. So we sat there till sundown feasting and drinking wine, and we looked across to the land of the Cyclops, and could see the smoke from their fires and hear their voices and the bleating of their flocks.

" Next morning at daybreak I called my men together, and told the rest to wait on the island while my crew and I went over to see what the Cyclops were like. So we rowed across to the mainland, and as we came near we saw a high cave by the shore. It was overhung with laurels, and in front was a courtyard fenced with a huge wall of stones and trunks of oak and towering pine. It was there that one of the Cyclops penned his flocks at night, and there he lived all alone among them: and a strange monster he was: he had only one eye in the middle of his forehead and he looked more like a wooded mountain-peak than a mortal man.

" Then I chose the twelve best of my company, leaving the others to guard the ship, and went up with them to the giant's cave. I put some food in a wallet and filled a goatskin full of a strong red wine I had with me, a wonderful fragrant wine that no man could resist. We soon reached the cave but found no one there, for the Cyclops was still away at the pasture. So we went in and looked at what he kept in his home. There were folds crowded with lambs and kids, and piles of wicker-baskets loaded with cheeses, and milk-pails, and bowls brimful of whey. Then my comrades begged me to take some of the cheeses and drive off the lambs and kids to our ship, and hurry away. Better if we had! But I would not listen. I wanted to see the giant and ask him for a gift. So we lit a fire and ate some of the cheeses and waited.

" At nightfall he came home with his herds, carrying a huge bundle of faggots to make a fire for supper. He flung them down on the floor with a crash, and we ran away from him into the depths of the cave. Then he drove in the ewes, leaving the rams outside in the yard, and he lifted up an enormous stone, so heavy that twenty teams could not hoist it from the ground, and set it in the mouth of the cave. After that he milked the sheep and the goats and curdled half the milk, putting the rest aside for his drink, and then he lit up the fire and caught sight of us and shouted:

" ' Who are you, strangers? Pirates or merchants?

And where have you come from, along the paths of the sea?'

"Our hearts sank within us when we heard his deep voice and saw what a monster he was, but I answered:

"'We are Greeks, warriors of Agamemnon's host, homeward bound from Troy across the fathomless waters. We have been driven out of our course by foul weather, and now we have come to you, and we beg you to treat us as your guests. Reverence the Gods, noble sir; for all guests and suppliants are avenged by Zeus.'

"But he only said, 'You are a fool, stranger, or else you have come from far indeed. We Cyclops pay no heed to Zeus nor any of the Gods; we are far stronger than they. No fear of his anger would make me spare your friends or you unless I chose. But now tell me where you have left your ship.'

"But I saw through the snare, and gave him a cunning answer:

"'Poseidon, the earth-shaker, wrecked our ship on the rocks, and we are the only men who were saved.'

"At that he sprang up without a word, and seized two of my comrades like whelps, and dashed their heads on the ground, and then he tore them limb from limb and devoured them like a mountain-lion, flesh and bones and all. And we wept at the horror and prayed to Zeus, but we found no way of escape. So the Cyclops filled his maw and then lay down full length on the ground among his flocks and fell asleep. Then I thought I would draw my sword and go up to him and feel for his heart with my hand and strike him dead; but I stopped, for I remembered that if I killed him we should only perish too, since none of us could roll away the enormous stone. So we had to wait there in our misery all night long.

" Day came at last, and the Cyclops awoke. He lit a fire and milked his ewes and seized two more of us for his meal, and then he drove out the sheep and goats, lifting away the stone and putting it back like the lid on a quiver. And off he went to the mountains whistling to his herd, and I was left to scheme for our revenge. And at last I thought of a plan. The giant had put a great club of his in the cave to dry. It was the trunk of an olive-tree and as big as a tall ship's mast. I cut off a fathom's length and we smoothed it down and sharpened the point and hardened it in the fire, and hid it away out of sight, for I meant to drive it into the monster's eye when he lay asleep. Then we cast lots to see who should help me, and the lot fell on the four I would have chosen myself.

" In the evening he came back again with his flocks, and this time he drove them all into the cave; and afterwards he sat down and milked the ewes and seized two more of us for his meal. Then I filled a wooden bowl with the wine I had brought, and I went up to him and said:

" ' Look, Cyclops, here is some wine to end your meal. Taste it and see what we carried in our ship. I brought it for you in hope you would take pity on us and let us go, but you have no mercy. Think, what man will ever come near you again if you show this cruelty? '

" So he took the wine and drank it, and it pleased him hugely, and he asked me for another draught.

" ' Give me some more,' he said, ' and tell me your name, and I will give you something to please you in return. We have grapes in our own land, but this wine is nectar.'

" Then I brought the wine, and three times I poured it out for him, and three times he drank it off in his folly. And when the wine began to cloud his wits, I said to him softly, " Cyclops, I will tell you my name, and you must give me the gift you promised. Noman is my name; Noman is what my father and mother call me and all my friends.'

" But he only said, ' I will eat Noman last and his comrades first. That shall be his gift.'

" With that he rolled over on his back and lay there fast asleep, his huge neck on one side. Then I thrust the stake into the embers and waited until it grew red-hot, cheering on my comrades all the time. And when the bar was just about to catch, we drew it out, and the four took hold of it and drove it into the monster's eye, while I stood at the end and turned it round and round, until everything was burnt away. The giant gave a terrible cry, so that the whole cliff rang, and we rushed back in terror, and he tore the bar out of his eye and flung it away, maddened with the pain. Then he shouted to the Cyclops who lived near him on the windy mountain-peaks. They heard his cries and gathered round the cave, and asked him, 'What ails you, Polyphemus? Why have you awakened us from our sleep, shouting

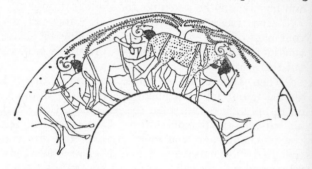

through the silence of the night? Has someone driven off your flocks or tried to murder you?'

"And Polyphemus answered, 'O, my friends, Noman is murdering me.'

"Then they replied, 'If no man has hurt you, we cannot save you from the sickness the Gods have sent. Pray to our father Poseidon.'

"So they went away, and I laughed to myself as I saw how my cunning had saved us. Then the giant groped his way to the mouth of the cave, moaning in his agony, and moved aside the stone and sat there with outstretched hands to catch us if we tried to pass; he thought I would be such a fool.   But I sat and pondered what to do, turning over many a plan in my head, for all our lives were at stake; and at last I resolved on this.   The rams were big and strong and their fleece was thick: I bound them together in threes, tying them with the withies on which the monster slept, and under each one in the middle I fastened a man, so that he was guarded on either side.   I had chosen the strongest in the flock for myself, and after all my comrades were safely fastened, I took hold of his back and curled myself round under his belly and held on tight to his great shaggy fleece; and we waited in this plight for the dawn.

" At last the morning broke, and then the rams went out to the pastures, while the ewes stayed near the folds, bleating to be milked.   Their master felt along the backs of the rams as they passed before him; but he had not the wit to guess that the men were bound underneath.   At the end, after the rest, came the one that carried me; my weight had made him slow.   Polyphemus stroked him lovingly, and said, ' Dear ram, why are you the last to-day?   You have always been the first before,—first to crop the flowers and the fresh young grass, first at the stream, first to hurry home again at night,—but now you are the last of all.   Are you grieving for your master whom a wicked man has blinded?   If you could only understand and had a voice to tell me where he is

skulking now, I would dash his head on the ground
and scatter his brains all over the rock, and get
some comfort in my misery.'

"Then he let the ram go out. And when we were
a little way off I slipped down and unfastened my
comrades, and we drove the fat rams before us and
hurried to our ships. The others were full of joy to
see us again; only they mourned for those we had
lost. But I hastened them on board and would not
give them time to weep, and we took our places on
the benches and struck our oars into the foam. But
just before we were out of earshot I called to the
Cyclops: 'Cyclops, it was no weakling whose comrades you devoured! And now the Gods have
punished you for all your cruelty.'

"Then his anger burst forth and he tore off the
top of a mountain and hurled it down at us. It fell
just beyond the ship, and the sea dashed up so that
the backwash drove us to the shore; but I seized
a pole and pushed off again, and then I shouted to
him once more, though my comrades tried to stop me:

"'Cyclops, if anyone asks who disfigured and
blinded you, tell them it was Odysseus, the son of
Laertes, who dwells in Ithaca.'

"Then Polyphemus groaned and said, 'Alas! The
old oracle is fulfilled. A prophet told me long ago
that Odysseus would take my sight from me; but
I always looked for a great and valiant hero, and
now it has been a puny nobody who deceived me
and made me drunk.'

" Then he lifted his hands to the starry heaven and called upon Poseidon:

" ' Hear me, Poseidon, enfolder of the earth, blue-haired God of the sea! If I am indeed your son, grant this prayer of mine. May Odysseus never see his home again! Or if that cannot be, and he is fated to return, let it be after many years, after the loss of all his comrades, on a foreign ship, in wretchedness, to find suffering and trouble in his home.'

" That was the Cyclops' prayer, and the blue-haired Sea-God heard him. But we escaped for the time and reached the island in safety, where we found our comrades on the beach, waiting for us anxiously. We told them all that had happened and they wept bitterly for the dead. That night we slept on shore, but at sunrise we went on board again, and rowed out once more over the waste of the grey sea."

CHAPTER X

HOW ODYSSEUS WAS ENTERTAINED BY CIRCE

" AND we came to the floating island where Æolus lives, the friend of the immortal Gods: all round it runs a barrier wall of bronze, and the cliffs fall sheer to the sea. There sits Æolus feasting in his palace with his six sons and six daughters, and the halls are full of the steam of the banquet, and the court-yard echoes all day long. He heard our story and entertained us kindly; and at parting he gave me a leather sack, in which he had shut up all the winds, tying the mouth with a silver cord. For the Gods have made him keeper of the winds, so that he can bind or loose them when he pleases. Only he set the West wind free, to carry our ship homewards.

" So nine days we sailed, and on the tenth our native country came in sight; and now we were so near that we could see the beacon-fires, when a deep sleep fell upon me; for I would let no one manage the sail but myself and I was tired out with the work. Then my companions began to whisper together, thinking that there was gold and silver in the sack; and they said to one another:

" ' See how much Odysseus is loved and honoured

wherever he goes. He is bringing many treasures home from Troy, while we who have made the journey too must return with empty hands. And now Æolus has given him all this wealth! Let us open the sack and see how much gold and silver he has got.'

"So they undid the cord, and out rushed all the winds and swept them back to sea. Then I awoke, and I could have found it in my heart to leap overboard and drown myself; but I hardened myself to bear it, and lay in the ship with my face muffled, while the winds drove us back to the island of Æolus.

"There we landed, and I went with two of my men up to the palace, and found the king feasting in the hall with his wife and children round him. We sat down on the threshold, and they all looked at us in amazement and asked what ill-fortune had befallen us. And I answered sadly, 'The folly of my comrades and my own sleep have been our ruin: help me, friends, for you have the power.' But they all were silent, while their father said: 'Get you gone from the island quickly, for I must give no help to one whom the Immortals hate.' With that he drove us from the house; and we launched our ship and rowed on, till the crew were wearied out, for we had no longer a wind to fill our sails.

"Then we came to the country of the Giants, the land where dawn follows close on darkness, so close that one shepherd as he drives his flocks afield can hail his fellow returning home. And there I lost all my ships but one. We saw the Giants' city with its mighty gates and we rowed up to the harbour, a quiet bay with a narrow mouth and steep cliffs on either hand. I moored my own ship to a rock at the entrance, but the other captains steered inside. The Giants caught sight of them and rushed out on the cliffs, hurling down enormous rocks, till they sank the ships, and then they speared the men like fishes. At once I cut the hawsers and called on my crew to row for their lives, and so we escaped ourselves, but all the rest were lost.

"Then we sailed on sadly, grieving for our comrades, till at last we came to the island where Circe lives, the bright-haired daughter of the Sun: she is a Goddess with magic power, but her voice is the voice of a mortal woman. There we found good harbour, and ran the ship ashore in silence, and lay on the beach two days and two nights, for we were worn out with our sorrows and our labour. But when the third morning rose, I took my spear and sword and set out, in the hope that I might find some trace of men. I went up to the top of a craggy hill, and from there I saw the whole island beneath me, covered with forest and thick woodlands, and in the middle of them I could see smoke going up from the house of Circe. At that I doubted for a while whether I should go and search further, but at last I thought it better to go back first to the ship and find food for my companions. Then some God had pity on me in my loneliness; for when I drew near the ship a noble stag with branching antlers came right across my path, going down from his pasture in the woods to drink at the stream. As he came up from the water I hurled my spear and struck him in the back, and he fell in the dust with a sob. Then I broke off willow boughs, and plaited a rope with which I tied his feet together, and so I brought him to the ship, carrying him across my back and leaning on my spear; for I could not carry him on my shoulder with one hand, he was such a size. I threw him down before the ship and shouted to my comrades:

" ' Courage, friends! In spite of all our troubles we shall not go down to the House of Death before our time. Come, let us eat, for we still have food and drink.'

" At my words they roused themselves and looked up, and wondered at the size of the stag; for he was a splendid beast. So we made a noble banquet and sat all day long till sunset, feasting on sweet wine and meat as much as we could wish; and when darkness came we lay and slept within sound of the sea.

" But in the morning I called them all together and said, ' It is time for us now to consider what way of safety lies open; for my part I see none. We have lost reckoning of which is east and which is west; and yesterday I went up to the top of a hill and saw that this place is an island and that the wide sea lies all round it as far as the eye can reach; I saw, too, smoke in the middle of the island going up through the forest-trees.'

" At these words their hearts sank, for they remembered what they had suffered from the cruel Cyclops; but they got no good for all their weeping. I divided my company into two bands, and over

each band I set a captain, myself over one and Eurylochus over the other. Then we cast lots in a brazen helmet, and the lot fell on Eurylochus. So he set off, and with him two and twenty men. They went up through the valleys, and in an open glade they came upon the house of Circe. It was all built of polished stone; and round it were lions and mountain-wolves, whom the Goddess had bewitched by the power of her magic drugs. My men were frightened at the sight, but the beasts did them no harm; only they stood on their hind legs and fawned upon them, wagging their long tails, like dogs round their master at supper-time. Now while my men stood waiting in the porch, they could hear Circe singing sweetly inside the house, and they could see her as she worked at a wonderful loom, weaving such rare and delicate work as the immortal Goddesses can fashion. Then Polites, the best and trustiest of them all, said to the rest:

" ' Friends, there is someone in the house, going up and down before a great loom, and singing so sweetly that all the hall rings with her song. Is it a woman or a Goddess? Let us call and make her hear.'

" So they called out to her; and she came at once and opened the shining doors, and bade them enter; and in their folly they obeyed. Only Eurylochus stayed outside, for he feared some mischief. She led them in and made them sit down on chairs and couches, and prepared for them a drink of wine and yellow honey, with cheese and barleymeal; but in it she mixed deadly drugs to make them forget their own country. Now when she had given them the cup and they had drunk, suddenly she struck them with a wand, and they were changed to swine. They grunted like swine, and they had the snouts and bristles of swine, but they still kept the minds of men. So they were shut up in the sty, lamenting; and Circe threw before them beechnuts and acorns, the fitting food of swine.

" But Eurylochus came back to the ship to bring the news of their unhappy fate; and at first he could not speak for grief, but at last when we pressed him he told us what had happened. ' We went up through the wood, as you commanded, noble Odysseus: and there in an open glade we found a stately building, and within it someone, a woman or a Goddess, singing sweetly and going up and down before a loom. The others called out to her, and she opened the shining doors and bade them enter, and they followed in their thoughtlessness and disappeared altogether: nor was any sign of them to be seen, though I sat and waited long.'

"When I heard this, I slung about my shoulder my bow and my great silver-studded sword, and ordered Eurylochus to lead the way; but he fell at my knees and said, 'Leave me here, I entreat you, and do not drag me to that place again: for I am sure that you will never bring back any of our comrades, nor yet return yourself. Better to escape at once with those that are here, while there is still time for flight.'

"But I answered, 'Stay here, if you like, Eurylochus, and eat and drink: but I must go, for I have no choice.'

"With that I left the ship and went up into the enchanted valleys; and as I came near the house of the sorceress a young man met me, in the bloom of youth, with the first down on his chin; and I knew him for the God Hermes, the bearer of the golden wand. He clasped my hand and said to me:

"'Where are you going, unhappy man, all alone through the glens, in a country that you do not know? Do you hope to set your comrades free? They are changed to swine, and imprisoned in the house of Circe; and you yourself would fare as they have done, if it were not that I will deliver you from

your peril. See, take this magic herb with you
when you go into her house, and it will protect you
from harm. And I will tell you of all her wicked
plans: she will mix you an enchanted drink and
afterwards she will strike you with her wand. Then
you must draw your sword and rush upon her as
though you meant to kill her, and she will be afraid
and implore you to be her friend: but before you
promise, you must make her swear a solemn oath by
the blessed Gods that she will do you no harm when
she finds you off your guard.'

" Then he plucked from the ground that magic
herb and showed me its nature. Its root is black
but its flower milk-white, and the Gods call it 'moly':
men find it hard to gather, but the Gods can do what
they will.

" Then Hermes vanished among the woodlands,
and I went on my way to the house of Circe, with
dark thoughts in my heart. I stood in the porch and
called out, and the Goddess heard my voice, and she
came and opened the shining doors and bade me
enter. She led me in and made me sit down on a
chair of silver work, with a footstool for my feet;
and then she mixed me drink in a golden cup, and in
it she put a charm to work me mischief. Now when
she had given me the cup and I had drunk it, she
struck me suddenly with her wand and cried; ' Off
to the sty, and lie there with your friends!' But I
drew my sword and rushed upon her, as though I
meant to kill her: and she gave a loud cry, and

ran in and caught my knees, and sobbed, ' Who
are you, strange man? And of what race do you
spring? There is no other man on earth who has
resisted the power of my drugs, once they have
passed his lips. Surely you must be that wise Odysseus, of whom Hermes told me, that he would come
to me some day on his journey home from Troy.
Nay, sheath your sword, and be my friend.'

" But I answered, ' O Circe, how can you bid me
treat you kindly? You have turned my friends to
swine within this hall, and now you would beguile
me in the hope that you may take me off my guard.
There can be no friendship between us, unless you
will swear a solemn oath that you will do me no more
harm.' So I spoke, and she took an oath as I commanded.

" Now there are four maid-servants who do the
work in Circe's house: they are the children of the
springs and the woods and the lonely rivers that flow
towards the sea. One of them spread purple coverlets upon the chairs, and another brought silver
tables and golden baskets for our feast. A third
mixed sweet wine in a silver bowl and set ready
golden cups; and the fourth prepared me a bath of
warm water, to take away the weariness from my
limbs. Then when I had bathed myself, and was
clothed in a fresh doublet and cloak, she led me back
to the hall, and meat and drink were set before me;
but I had no taste for food, and my thoughts were
far away.

" When Circe saw me sitting thus, she came and said to me, ' What is the matter, Odysseus? Why do you sit like a dumb man, not touching food or drink? Are you still afraid of treachery? You need not fear me now, for I have sworn you a binding oath.' And I answered, ' How can I have any heart for food until I have set my comrades free and seen them face to face! '

" Then she took her wand and went through the hall and opened the doors of the sty, and drove out things that looked like swine, and I knew them for my comrades. But she went among them where they stood, and sprinkled each of them with another charm; and the bristles dropped from their limbs, and they became men again, younger than they had been before, and comelier far and taller to behold. They knew me and clasped my hands, while the tears fell from their eyes, so that the Goddess herself felt pity; and she said to me, ' Go down to the beach, Odysseus, and draw up the ship and store your goods and tackle in a cave; then come back here, and bring all your company with you.'

" So I went down to the ship and found my companions sitting there with heavy hearts; but when they saw me they thronged round me, and they were comforted as though they had come back to their own country, rugged Ithaca, where they were born. Then they asked me how the rest had perished: but I said, ' Draw the ship on land, and follow me, and you shall see our friends eating and drinking in

the house of Circe, where there are good things
enough and to spare.'

"And they were ready to obey, but Eurylochus
said to them, 'Here is fresh trouble for us! Are you
so bent on danger that you must go to the house of
Circe, who will turn us all into swine or wolves or
bears, to guard her great house and be her prisoners?
Remember how it happened in the land of the
Cyclops, when Odysseus led our comrades into the
cave, and through his rashness they met their death.'

"At this I grew so angry that I could have drawn
my sword and hewn his head from his body, though
he was my own near kinsman: but the others came
between us and said, 'Lead the way to Circe's house
and leave him here alone.' So they all went with
me; and Eurylochus followed too, when he saw that
he would be left alone, for he was afraid of my
rebuke.

"When we came to Circe's house, we found the
others sitting at a rich banquet; and my companions
wept for joy to see one another again. Then Circe
came and stood by my side, and said to them, 'Do
not weep any longer: I know you have had trouble
enough by land and sea. But now you must eat and
drink, until you have forgotten your wanderings and
your hearts are young again within you as on the
day when you left Ithaca long ago.'

"So there we lived in all comfort until a whole
year had passed: but at the year's end my comrades
called me apart, and bade me remember our native

country.   Then in the evening I went to Circe's
chamber and put her in mind of her promise, and
told her how my heart and the hearts of all my company were set upon returning home. And the Goddess
answered, ' I will not keep you here, Odysseus,
against your will. But before you see your home,
you have another journey to make, for you must
visit the House of Death and ask counsel from the
spirit of Teiresias, the blind old prophet of Thebes:
he alone has kept his wisdom even in the other
world, where all the rest are flitting shadows.'

" When I heard this my heart sank, and I no
longer wished to look upon the sun: but at last I
said, ' Who will be my pilot, Circe, upon such a
voyage? No ship has ever touched that shore.'

" Then the Goddess answered, ' Son of Laertes,
you will have no need of any pilot. Raise the mast
and set the sails, and rest in your places; and the
North wind will bear you of itself. You will come
to the stream of Ocean, and beyond it you will reach
a desolate shore, where tall poplars grow and the
willows which lose their fruit. Beach your ship there
beside the deep eddies of Ocean, and go to the
House of Death. There you must dig a pit a yard
four-square, and pour three times a drink-offering to
the dead, honey and wine and water; and you must
sprinkle barley-meal upon it, and sacrifice a ram and
a black ewe. Soon the spirits of the dead will rise
and throng about you; but you must draw your
sword and not suffer any of them to come near

the sacrifice, until you have held counsel with Teiresias.'

"Thus we talked through the night, and when morning came I roused my comrades, and said to them, 'Awake and let us be upon our way: such is Circe's bidding. But before we see our home we have another journey to make, for we must visit the House of Death and take counsel of the spirit of Teiresias.' Their hearts sank within them at my words, but their weeping brought no good: so we went with heavy thoughts toward the sea. There by the black ship Circe met us and made fast a ram and a ewe; and immediately she vanished from our sight."

CHAPTER XI

HOW ODYSSEUS VISITED THE HOUSE OF DEATH

" So we went on board and set sail with a favouring wind. We made the ship trim and sat down to rest, while the wind and the steersman guided us on, till at night we came to that deep-flowing stream of Ocean that circles all the world. There the Cimmerians live in mist and cloud and never see the sun, for a deadly night hangs over their land. We passed them by and went on to the place which Circe had told us of, and there I bade two of my companions take the sheep and hold them ready for the sacrifice, while I drew my sword and dug a pit a yard four-square, and in it I poured a drink-offering to the dead, honey and wine and water, and sprinkled barley over it. And I prayed to Persephone, the pure and awful Goddess of the Underworld, and took the victims and cut their throats and let the dark blood flow forth.

" Then the spirits of the dead came out from their dwelling-place and gathered round me, but I drew my sword and would not let them touch the blood till I had inquired of Teiresias. My mother's

D 10

spirit came to me, Anticleia, whom I left alive when I set out for Troy, and I wept when I saw her; but for all my sorrow I would not let her touch the blood till I had seen Teiresias.

"And at last came the old seer of Thebes, bearing a golden sceptre in his hand, and he knew me and said, 'Why have you come here, Odysseus, leaving the light of day for this cheerless land? If you will let me draw near and taste the blood, I will tell you what you wish to know."

"So I sheathed my sword and let him draw near and drink, and when he had drunk, he said, 'You seek to know of your return, noble Odysseus. The lord of the sea, Poseidon, will make it hard and painful, for he is wroth with you because you blinded the Cyclops, his son. But even so you may all return after much suffering, if you can restrain yourself and your companions from touching the cattle of the Sun, when you reach the Beautiful Island where they graze. Do them no hurt and you may all reach Ithaca again; but if you harm them, your ship and your company will perish, and though you may escape yourself, you will return alone, in wretchedness, after many years and on a stranger's ship. And you will find trouble in your house, lawless men who devour your substance and woo your wife. Yet you will subdue them by craft, or by the sword, and slay them in your halls, and avenge their violence. And after that is done you must set out once more: you must take an oar upon your shoulder and journey through many lands, till you come to a people who have never heard of the sea, and do not know what an oar is like. And when you meet a man who asks if you have a winnowing-fan on your shoulder, then you must stop and fix your oar in the ground and offer sacrifice to King Poseidon. So shall you make your peace with him and with all the Gods, and you shall have rest at last and your people shall be happy. And death will come to you at last from the sea, the gentlest death of all, when your strength is gone at the end of a calm old age.'

"And I answered, 'Teiresias, let the Gods' will be done! But tell me, I pray you, this one thing more. I see my mother's spirit there, sitting in silence near the blood and not raising her eyes nor speaking to her son. How can I make her know me?'

"And he replied, 'Let those you choose come near the blood and drink, and they will answer you truly. And those that you reject will go away.'

"Then the spirit of Teiresias went back to the House of Death, and I stood there waiting till my mother came and drank the dark blood; and at once she knew me and said to me in pity:

"'My child, how have you come into this darkness alive? It is hard for living men to find the way. Is it from Troy you come, and have you wandered with your comrades ever since the war? Have you not been home to Ithaca, nor seen your wife?'

"Then I said: 'Mother, I needed the counsel of Teiresias, the seer of Thebes. I have not touched the shores of Greece, but have wandered and suffered ever since I went with Agamemnon to fight at Troy. But tell me, mother, of yourself. What death brought you here? Was it slow disease, or the arrows of Artemis that kill and do not hurt? And what of my father? And my son whom I left behind? Are they still masters in my home, or have they lost hope of my return and let another take my place? And tell me of my wife, does she still guard the house for me or has she married the best of the Grecian lords?'

"And my mother answered, 'She is true and faithful, and guards your house, and sorrows for you always, day and night; and Telemachus is honoured on your lands and at the feast. But your father never comes to the city. He stays on his farm, and in winter he sleeps with the labourers in the ashes by the fire. He has no rugs nor blankets, and only wretched clothing to put on, and when the warm summer comes, he has a bed of fallen leaves in a corner of the vineyard. There he lies, nursing his sorrow, and longing for your return; and he ages fast with grief. It was grief like his that brought me here, and not wasting sickness nor the gentle arrows of Artemis. I longed for you, Odysseus, for your wisdom and your tenderness, and I longed for you till I died.'

"And as she spoke, my heart went out to her, and I sprang forward to take her in my arms. Three times I sprang towards her, and three times she flitted from my arms, like a shadow or a dream. It wrung my heart, and I cried, 'Mother, why will you not stay? Let us put our arms round each other even here, and weep out our hearts. Or can it be that dread Persephone has sent a phantom to mock me and make me grieve still more?'

"But my mother answered, 'No, my child, all mortals when they die must be as I am now. Fire burns away the bones and flesh and sinews as soon as life is gone, and the spirit flies away and hovers like a dream. But hasten back to the light of the sun and tell your wife what you have seen.'

"And so we talked together, and the dread queen sent other noble women from the House of Death, the wives and daughters of the heroes, more than I can tell of; for the night is passing and it is time for sleep and to-morrow I must depart."

Odysseus ceased, and they all sat silent and spellbound in the shadowy hall, till Arete said: "My lords, we see now that the stranger is wise as he is comely. He is my guest, but all of you may share in honouring him. So do not hasten him away, but give him gifts of all the treasure you have stored at home."

Then Alcinous said, "As I am king of the land, it shall be done. Let the stranger stay till to-morrow and I will complete his escort and his gift."

And Odysseus said, "King Alcinous, I would gladly stay a whole year long, if you would give me a safe return and splendid gifts."

And Alcinous made answer, " The grace of speech is on your lips, Odysseus, and wisdom is in your heart. We honour you and hear you gladly, and your tale is like a cunning minstrel's song. But we would fain hear one thing more. Did you not see among the spirits any of the heroes who went with you to Troy? Tell us of these, I pray you, for the night is still young, and for myself I could listen to you till the dawn."

Then Odysseus spoke again: " King Alcinous, there is a time for tales and a time for sleep: but if you would still hear more, I will tell you of my comrades who perished after they had returned from Troy.

" When Persephone had called back the spirits of the noble women, I saw the ghost of Agamemnon come forth and all his followers. He knew me at once, and wept to see me and stretched out his hands to touch me. But there was no strength in his limbs. I pitied him and said, ' Tell me, leader of men, what death laid you low? Did Poseidon wreck your ships, or did you fall in some raid on land? '

" And Agamemnon answered, ' Not so, Odysseus: it was Ægisthus slew me, Ægisthus and my accursed wife. They slew me at a feast in my own palace, without pity, like an ox in the stall. Of all the slaughter you have ever seen, you would have sorrowed most at that. We lay dying in the hall where the tables were spread and the wine mixed for the feast, and all the floor ran blood. I raised my hands to that shameless woman before **I** died, but she turned away and would not even close my eyes; and I had thought to come back welcome to my children and my home. So I bid you never be gentle to a woman nor tell all that is in your heart even to your wife, for there is no faith in womankind. But you, Odysseus, will not die at the hand of Penelope, for she is faithful and wise: well I remember her, a young wife with a baby at her breast, when we went away to Troy. He must be a grown man now and he will meet his father and kiss him on his return; but my wife would not even let me see my son again before she slew me.'

" Then he asked me if I had heard of his son Orestes, where he was; but I could not tell him. And so we stood talking and sorrowing, till others came, Achilles the swift-footed, and Ajax, the strongest and fairest of the rest. Achilles saw me and said, ' Man of many adventures, what daring enterprise is this? How could you brave the House of Death and all the empty phantoms of the dead? '

" And I replied, ' I came, renowned Achilles, to take counsel of Teiresias, how I might reach my home in Ithaca again; for I have not touched the shores of Greece nor set my foot on my native soil. I wander and suffer still, but you have a happier fate, for we honoured you as a God in your lifetime, and now you are a prince among the dead.'

" But he answered, ' That is vain comfort, Odysseus. I would sooner be a poor man's slave and live on earth, than rule all the kingdoms of the dead. But tell me of my son and my father, the hero Peleus. Do the people honour him still, or is he despised and neglected now that he is old? For I am not there to fight for him as I fought for the Greeks at Troy; I cannot come back to his house for a day and drive the usurpers before me.'

"Then I told him all I knew: I could give him no tidings of his father, but I told him how I had brought his son in my own ship to Troy and how he was foremost in the battle but escaped unwounded, and how he was one of the comeliest of the chiefs, and wise and ready in debate. And Achilles rejoiced to hear of his son's renown and strode away with long steps through the meadow of asphodel.

"And I saw other spirits of dead heroes standing round, sorrowful but wishing to speak to me. Only Ajax stood apart and would not speak, for he was wroth with me because I had contended with him for the arms of Achilles and vanquished him and won the prize. Better that I had never won it and that the noble Ajax were still alive! So I spoke softly to him, to turn away his wrath, but he answered not a word and went back to the other spirits in the House of Death.

"And I might have seen many another famous hero and would have seen them gladly. But ere they came, a strange cry arose, and the countless multitudes of the dead thronged about me, brides and youths unmarried, and old men who had suffered long, and tender maidens with fresh grief at heart, and warriors in their bloodstained armour.

"Then fear came upon me, and I hurried back to the ship and bade my men loose her and take to their oars; and we rowed across the stream of Ocean, and there a favouring wind sprang up and bore us on our way."

CHAPTER XII

HOW ODYSSEUS PASSED BY THE SIRENS AND SCYLLA

"So we left the stream of Ocean and sailed away across the open sea back to Circe's island, to the land of sunrise and the palaces of Dawn. There we beached our ship on the sand and stepped ashore, and Circe came to welcome us, bringing bread and meat and sparkling wine. We gathered round her and she said to us all:

"'O daring adventurers! Have you gone down alive to the House of Death? Have you chosen to die twice though other men die but once? But now you shall eat and drink and rest for to-day, and to-morrow morning you may set sail once more, when I have told you the way you must go and the dangers you have to meet.'

"So we sat down with her and feasted there till sunset. And when the darkness came my comrades went to sleep beside the ship, but Circe took me apart and asked me what I had seen; and I told her everything, and at the close she said:

"'So that journey is accomplished, Odysseus, and now hearken to me and remember what I say. First you will come to the Sirens, the singers who charm all men with their song. The man who goes near to listen will never see his wife and children again, gathered round to welcome his return; he will stay in the Sirens' meadow and they will sit beside him, chanting their clear-toned song, among heaps of dead men's bones and withering flesh. You must row past them steadily, and stop the ears of your crew with wax; but if you want to hear the song yourself and know the delight of it, make your comrades bind you hand and foot to the mast, and should you beg them to set you free, they must bind you tighter than before.

" ' But when you have left the Sirens behind you, I cannot tell for certain which way you are to go, for your own wit must decide, and I can only tell you the dangers on either hand. On one side are the Hanging Rocks that the Gods call the Wanderers. Storms of fire sweep round them, the waves dash and roar at their feet, and dead bodies and broken spars lie heaving on the water. Only one ship has ever passed between in safety; the famous Argo of whom all men have heard, and even she would have been wrecked except for Hera's care. But if you turn away you will reach a narrow strait, only a bowshot wide. On one hand rises a towering cliff, so steep and sheer that no mortal man can climb it. Winter and summer a dark cloud hangs overhead, and below in the western face of the cliff there is a deep and murky cavern. Now there is no other way

Odysseus, and you must steer your ship close by. That cave is Scylla's lair, where she lies in wait, howling like a whelp; and a terrible monster she is that even the Gods might fear to face. She has twelve dangling feet, and six long necks, and on each neck a fearful head with three rows of deadly grinning teeth. She is sunk in the cavern up to her waist, but she stretches out her heads round the cliff fishing for dolphins and sea-dogs and all the monsters of the ever-moaning sea. No crew can boast that they have escaped unhurt, for she darts out whenever a ship passes by and seizes a man in every mouth.

" ' But across the strait you will see another rock, lower than the first. A great branching fig-tree grows above it, and underneath is Charybdis in her dark and roaring pool. Thrice a day she belches out the water and thrice a day she sucks it down again. Heaven send you are not within her reach when she sucks the water down! Poseidon himself could not save you then. So you must keep close to Scylla's rock and row past that way, for it is better to lose six of your crew than to perish with them all.'

" Then I said to Circe, ' Now tell me this, Goddess, and tell me truly: could I escape Charybdis and yet conquer Scylla too? '

" And the Goddess answered: ' Rash man, will nothing stop you? You only live to labour and to dare. Will you defy the immortal Gods themselves? She is deathless, and no man can fight with her; you must flee, for if you wait to put on your armour she will dart out again and carry off six more of your crew. Row past her as hard as you can, and call on the mother who bore her for a curse to men, and she will hold her back.

" ' And after that you will come to the Beautiful Island, the pasture-ground for the sheep and cows

of the Sun, who were never born and never die, and have fair-haired nymphs to tend them, Light-of-day and Shining-beam, the daughters of the Sun. Now if you leave the herds in peace you may all reach Ithaca again at last; but if you harm them your ship and your company will perish, and, even though you should escape yourself, you will return alone, in wretchedness, after many years.'

" Thus the night passed away, and when morning

broke I went down to the ship; and we took our places on board, and Circe sent a friendly breeze to fill our sails and help us. So we sat at ease while the ship ran on, and then I said to my crew:

" ' Comrades, you must all hear the counsel Circe gave me. She bade us beware of the Sirens and their magic song and the flowery meadow where they sit. I alone may listen, but you must bind me to the mast so that I cannot move, and if I beg you to set me free bind me tighter than before.'

" So the good ship went scudding on to the Sirens' island with the fair breeze in her wake, when suddenly the wind dropped and there was a dead calm; something had put the waves to rest. Then my crew hauled down the sails and took out the oars, and I made plugs of wax and stopped their ears with them, and they bound me hand and foot to the mast. And when we came within earshot of the shore the Sirens caught sight of the ship and began their magic song:

" ' Hither, come hither and hearken awhile, Odysseus, far-famed king!
No sailor ever has passed this way but has paused to hear us sing.
Our song is sweeter than honey, and he that can hear it knows
What he never had learnt from another, and has joy before he goes;
We know what the heroes bore at Troy in the ten long years of strife,
We know what happens in all the world, and the secret things of life.'

" I heard the wonderful music and my heart

longed to listen, and I made signs to my comrades
to set me free; but the others only bent to their
oars and rowed the harder, while two of them stood
up and bound me tighter than before, till at last we
had left the Sirens behind us and could not hear
their song, and then my comrades took out the wax
from their ears and unfastened me.

" But as soon as we were clear of the island we
saw smoke ahead of us and breakers, and heard the
thunder of the surf.   At that my comrades were
panic-stricken, and the oars dropped from their
hands, splashing into the water, so that the ship
stopped dead. But I went along the benches to
encourage them, and said:

" ' My friends, we have had danger to face before.
This is no worse than when the Cyclops shut us in
his cave, and yet I brought you out safe at last. We
shall live to look back on this adventure too. Row
on steadily, all of you. Hug the cliff, steersman, and
keep the ship from that smoke and surf.'

" So they took heart and obeyed me. But I would
not tell them about Scylla, for we could not fight
her, and I feared if they knew they might drop their
oars and hide themselves in the hold. And then I
found that one of Circe's counsels was too hard for
me; she had said I must not arm myself, but I put
on my harness and took a couple of spears in my
hand and went up on the prow to get the first sight
of the monster; but I could not see a sign of anything, though I strained my eyes till they were tired.

searching the face of the shadowy cliff. Thus we sailed up through the strait, Scylla on one side of us and the whirlpool on the other. When the water came belching out the whole pool seethed and boiled like a cauldron on the fire, and the spray dashed up high over the top of the cliff, and as it rushed back in the ebb we could see right down the spinning sides, to the dark sand underneath, a sight to turn us pale.

" But while we looked and trembled, suddenly Scylla darted out and snatched six of my crew, and I only turned in time to see their heads and feet in the air and to hear them call my name for the last time in their agony. But Scylla drew them to the rock, gasping, as a fisherman draws in the fish at the end of his line, and she devoured them at the very mouth of her den, while they cried to us and stretched out their hands in that awful struggle of death. That was the saddest sight I ever saw in all my wanderings over the sea.

" But the rest of us sailed away and left the strait behind, and then we came in sight of the Sun-God's beautiful island. And while we were still some way off I could hear the lowing of the cattle and the bleating of the flocks, and I remembered the warning of Circe and Teiresias, the blind old seer. So I begged my comrades not to land, but their spirits sank at the thought, and Eurylochus spoke out angrily:

" ' Have you no pity, Odysseus? Are you made of iron yourself, never weak and never tired? We

are wearied to death, and you will not let us land
here and take our food, but must drive us out again
to wander all night long over the blackening waters.
What if a storm should rise and wreck the ship?
The darkness is here already, and surely it would be
best to sleep on the shore to-night and to-morrow
we can set sail.'

" All the crew were on his side, so that I had to
yield, and we put in to shore, but I made them swear
a solemn oath not to touch the sacred herds. We
found a spring of sweet water near the beach and took
our supper beside it, and the men lay down to rest,
weeping for the comrades they had lost, till at last
sleep stopped their tears. But after midnight, when
the stars were sinking to the west, a terrible storm
arose, and in the morning we had to draw up the
ship into a hollow cave and wait for the wind to
fall. But it blew without ceasing from the south or
east a whole month long, and at last we had eaten
everything in the ship, and we tried to catch fish
and birds for ourselves, but we almost died of hunger.
And one day I had gone apart by myself to ask the
Gods for help, when I fell into a strange deep sleep,
and while I slept Eurylochus gave evil counsel to
the rest:

" ' Listen to me, my friends. Death is hateful in
any shape, but death by famine is the worst of all.
Come, let us choose the best of the herd and sacrifice
to the Gods. If we reach home again we can build
a stately temple to the Sun and fill it full of splendid

offerings; and even if he should be angry and wreck our ship, I would rather take one gulp of sea-water and die, than be slowly starved to death in a desolate place like this.'

"Thus he persuaded them, and they killed the fattest cows and made a burnt offering, roasting the flesh and eating to their heart's content; and when it was too late I woke from my heavy sleep and smelt the savoury smoke, and groaned, for I understood it all. And while I mourned, Shining-beam, the long-robed shepherd-nymph, went up with the news to her father, the great Sun-God. And he cried to the Immortals in his anger:

"'Father Zeus! And all you Gods of Heaven! Punish the comrades of Odysseus as they deserve! They have killed my cows, the cows that were my joy whenever I went up into the starry sky or turned to the earth again. Give me vengeance, or I will go down into the House of Death and shine among the ghosts.'

"Then Zeus begged him to stay and shine on earth for Gods and men, and promised he would hurl his white thunder-bolt on our ship and break it in mid-sea.

"Meanwhile I hurried back to my crew and upbraided them bitterly, but there was nothing to be done; the cattle were dead. And strange signs began to show themselves: the skins crept and the flesh moaned on the spits, and we heard sounds like the lowing of cows. Six more days we waited and

ate the roasted meat, but on the seventh the storm
sank at last, and we hoisted our white sails again and
stood out to sea. But when we were out of sight of
land—nothing round us but sea and sky—a black
cloud gathered overhead, darkening all the waves
below. For a while it hung there motionless, and
then suddenly the storm burst and the West wind
swooped whistling on the ship, tearing away the
forestays so that the mast crashed down on the
stern. It struck the helmsman in its fall, and his
skull was split by the blow, and he dropped from the
deck like a diver into the sea. Then thunder pealed
on every side, and the lightning struck the boat and
sent her reeling, and my men were washed overboard. For a few moments I saw them floating
round her like sea-gulls on the water, and then they
were swept away.

"But I stayed by the ship till the billows stripped
her sides from the naked keel, and then I lashed the
mast to it and so drifted before the gale. Soon to
my terror the wind veered round and blew from the
south, carrying me back to Charybdis and death.
All night I was blown along and as the sun rose I
came to the dreadful strait. It was the hour of the
ebb, but I made a spring and clutched the topmost
boughs of the fig-tree that overshadowed the pool,
and there I clung like a bat. I could get no foothold,
for the branches swung high in air and the roots
stretched far away below, and so I set my face and
hung on there, waiting for the whirlpool to throw

out the mast and keel again, and at last, in the afternoon, I saw the long timbers below me. Down I plunged in the water and got astride them, and there I sat and paddled myself along. Nine days I drifted thus, and on the tenth I came to the island where Calypso lives, the bright-haired Goddess who took me to her home and cared for me. But I told you about that yesterday, and why speak of it again? I have no love for a twice-told tale."

CHAPTER XIII

HOW ODYSSEUS REACHED ITHACA AND MET
ATHENA FACE TO FACE

WHEN Odysseus had finished his story, there was silence in the hall till Alcinous said, " Odysseus, now that you have come to my house after all these troubles, you shall return without more wandering to your home." And then he bade the princes go home for the night and meet again in the morning to bring their gifts.

So next day the Sea-kings went down to the ship and put their gifts on board and then returned to the palace and sacrificed an ox to Zeus. And there they feasted and drank their good wine till the sun went down. The minstrel sang to them, but Odysseus kept looking at the sun impatiently, like a hungry ploughman tired out at the close of day. At last the time arrived, and then Odysseus said, " Alcinous, let me go now, and fare you well. My escort and my gifts are all prepared and I could wish no more. May I but find my wife and my dear ones all safe and sound at home! And may Heaven grant you also happy homes and every blessing and no distress among your people!" And to Queen Arete

he said, "Lady, may you live happily with your
husband and children and all this people till old age
comes to you, and death, which must come to all!"

Then the herald led the way and Odysseus followed
to the ship, and the queen sent her servants with
him to carry warm clothing for the voyage and food
and drink. And when they had stored the ship he
lay down silently in the stern, and the rowers took
their places on the benches and plied their oars,
while a deep, sweet sleep fell upon him, like the sleep
of death. Then the wonderful ship leapt forward on
her way, like a chariot-team plunging beneath the
whip, and the great dark wave roared round the
stern. No hawk could fly so quickly as that ship
flew through the water, and the hawk is the swiftest
of all birds. And as she sped, the man who had
suffered so much, the man as wise as the Gods, lay
peacefully asleep and forgot his sufferings.

But when the bright star rose that tells the
approach of day, the ship came in sight of Ithaca.
There is a haven there between two headlands which
break the waves, so that ships can ride in safety
without a mooring-rope, and at the head of it an
olive-tree, and a shadowy cave where the water-
fairies come and tend their hives, and weave their
sea-blue garments on the hanging looms, and mix
their wine in bowls and jars of stone. There are
springs of water in the cavern, and two ways into
it, one to the North for men, and one to the South,
where none but the Gods may pass.

The Sea-kings knew this harbour and rowed straight into it, and ran their ship half a keel's length ashore. Then they lifted Odysseus out of the stern, wrapt in the rugs and coverlet, and laid him, still asleep, upon the sand. And the gifts they placed in a pile by the trunk of the olive-tree, a little out of the road, so that no passer-by might rob him as he slept.

Then they sailed away; and after they were gone Odysseus awoke, but he could not recognise the land where he lay, for Athena had cast a mist about him so that everything looked strange, though he was the lord of it all. There were the mountain-paths and the sheltering creeks, the high, steep rocks, and the trees in bloom; but he could not see it aright, and started up, smiting his hands upon his thighs, and cried aloud:

" What land have I come to now?   And what can I do with all this treasure?   If the Sea-kings did not really mean to take me back to Ithaca, they should have conveyed me to some other people who would have sent me home."   And then he counted the gifts over, the golden vessels and the beautiful garments, and found nothing missing, but they gave him no pleasure; and he turned sadly to walk along the shore and dream of home, when a young herdsman met him, of noble figure, with a javelin in his hand, and a fine mantle in double folds upon his shoulders. Odysseus was glad to greet him, and asked what country he had reached. It was Athena in disguise, and she answered, " Truly, stranger, you must have come from far indeed. For this is a famous island that all men know, whether they live in the east or in the west. It is a rugged land and no place for horses and chariots, but though it is narrow, it is not so poor; for there are stores of corn and wine, plenty of water for the cattle and plenty of wood. Its name is Ithaca, and some men have heard of it even at Troy, which they say is a long way off."

Then brave Odysseus rejoiced in his heart to hear that it was his native land; but he would not tell the herdsman who he was, and made up a cunning story that he had escaped as an outlaw from Crete and had been left upon the island by a Phoenician crew. And the Goddess smiled to hear him, and stood forth in her own true form, a wise and noble woman, tall and fair, and put her hand upon his shoulder and said:

" Come, let us practise no more craft on one another, Odysseus, for we are both famous for our wit and wiles, you among mortals and I among the Gods. I am Pallas Athena, daughter of Zeus, and I have stood beside you and protected you in all your wanderings and toil. And now I have come here to tell you of the troubles that await you in your house, and to help you with my counsel. For you must still endure in silence, and tell no one that Odysseus has returned."

And the king made answer, " It is hard, Goddess, for a mortal to know you, wise though he may

be, for you come in many shapes. Truly I have
known your kindness from of old in Troy, but when
we went on board the ships, I never saw you at my
side again. Tell me, I pray you, if this land is
indeed Ithaca, my home."

Then the Goddess answered, " I see, Odysseus,
that you keep your ready wit and steadfast mind.
I could not show myself your friend before for fear
of angering Poseidon, my own father's brother. But
come now, and I will show you Ithaca; there is the
haven and the olive with its slender leaves, and the
cave where you once made many an offering to the
water-nymphs."

And then she rolled away the mist and the long-
suffering hero saw his native land again. He kissed
the kindly earth, and vowed to the nymphs that he
would bring them offerings as of old if he lived to
see his dear son a man.

Then the Goddess bade him be of good cheer, and
showed him a hiding-place in the cavern for the
gifts. And then they sat down by the trunk of the
olive-tree, and Athena told him all the misdeeds of
the suitors, and how his wife had beguiled them and
kept them waiting till his return, and how he must
avenge himself and her.

Then Odysseus said, " Truly, I should have
perished in my own halls, like Agamemnon, if you
had not warned me. Help me, therefore, with your
wisdom, and stand beside me again, and put strength
and courage within me as in the days of Troy. For

with you by my side I could fight against thrice a hundred men."

And Pallas Athena made answer, " I will be with you, Odysseus, when the hour of conflict is come, and the blood of the suitors, who eat up your substance, shall be shed at last. But now I will change you into a poor beggar, so old and so wretched that no one will know you, and in that guise you must go and stay with the herdsman Eumaeus who tends your swine, until I have brought your son Telemachus from Sparta, where he is gone to seek tidings of you."

Then she touched him with her magic wand, and the fair flesh withered on his limbs and the golden locks fell from his head, and he was changed into an old man. His skin was shrivelled and his bright eyes dimmed, and for his covering she gave him a tattered wrap, begrimed with smoke, a worn deerskin on his shoulder and a wallet, and a staff in his hand.

Then she vanished, and left him to take his way alone across the hills.

CHAPTER XIV

HOW THE SWINEHERD WELCOMED ODYSSEUS

So Odysseus went up along the rough mountain-path, through the forest and over the hills, till he came to the house where his faithful steward lived. It stood in an open space, and there was a large courtyard in front, with a wall of heavy stones and thorn-boughs and a stout oak palisade. Inside the yard there were twelve styes for the pigs, and the swineherd kept four watch-dogs to guard the place, great beasts, and fierce as wolves, that he had reared himself. Odysseus found him at home, sitting in the porch alone, and cutting himself a pair of sandals from a well-browned oxhide.

The dogs caught sight of the king as soon as he came up, and flew at him, barking, but he had the wit to let go his staff and sit down at once on the ground. Still it might have gone hard with him there, in front of his own servant's house, had not Eumaeus rushed out of the porch, dropping the leather in his haste, and scolded the dogs, driving them off with a volley of stones.

Then he said to Odysseus, " A little more, old man, and the dogs would have torn you in pieces and disgraced me for ever! And I have my full share of trouble as it is, for I have lost the best master in all the world, and must sit here to mourn for him and fatten his swine for other men, while he is wandering somewhere in foreign lands, hungry and thirsty perhaps, if he is still alive at all. But now come in yourself, and let me give you food and drink, and tell me your own tale."

So he took Odysseus into the house, and made a seat for him with a pile of brushwood and a great thick shaggy goatskin which he used for his own bed, and all with so kind a welcome that it warmed the king's heart till he prayed the Gods to bless him for his goodness. But Eumaeus only said, " How could I neglect a stranger, though he were a worse man than you? All strangers and beggars are sent to us by Zeus. Take my gift and welcome; though it is little enough I have to give, a servant such as I, with new masters to lord it over him. For we have lost the king who would have loved me and given me house and lands and all that a faithful servant ought to have, whose work is blest by the Gods and prospers, as mine does here. Alas! he is dead and gone! He went away with Agamemnon to fight at Troy and never came home again."

So saying, the good swineherd rose and fetched what meat and wine he had, and set it before Odysseus, grieving that he had nothing better for him because the shameless suitors plundered everything.

But Odysseus ate and drank eagerly, and when

his strength had come again he asked Eumaeus, " My friend, who is this master of yours you tell me of? Did you not say he was lost for Agamemnon's sake? Perhaps I may have seen him, for I have travelled far."

But the swineherd answered, " Old man, his wife and son will believe no traveller's tale. They have heard too many such. Every wandering beggar who comes to Ithaca goes to my mistress with some empty story to get a meal for himself, and she welcomes him and treats him kindly, and asks him about it all, with the tears running down her cheeks in a woman's way. Yes, even you, old man, might learn to weave such tales, if you thought they would get you a cloak or a doublet. No, he is dead, and dogs and birds have eaten him, or else he has fed the fishes, and his bones lie somewhere on the seashore, buried in the sand. And he has left us all to grieve for him, but no one more than me, who can never have so kind a master again, not though I had my heart's desire and went back to my native land, and saw my father and mother and the dear home where I was born. It is Odysseus above all whom I long to see once more. There, stranger, I have called him by his name, and that I should not do; for he is still my dear master, though he is far away."

Then Odysseus said, " My friend, your hope has gone, and so you will never believe me. But I tell you this, and I seal it with an oath:—Odysseus will return! Poor as I am, I will take no reward for my news till he comes to his own again, but you shall give me a new doublet and cloak that day, and I will wear them."

But the swineherd answered, "Ah, my friend, I shall never need to pay you that reward. He will never come back again. But now drink your wine in peace, and let us talk of something else; and do not call to mind the sorrow that almost breaks my heart. Tell me of yourself and your own troubles, and who you are, and what ship brought you here, for you will not say you came afoot."

Then Odysseus pretended he was a Cretan who had fought at Troy, and he told Eumaeus a long tale of adventures and how he had been wrecked at last on the coast of Epirus. The king of the country, he said, had rescued him, and he had learned that Odysseus had been there a little while before, and was already on his way to Ithaca.

The swineherd listened eagerly to it all, but when Odysseus had finished he said, "Poor friend, my heart aches to hear of all your sufferings. But there is one thing you should not have said, one thing I can never believe, and that is that Odysseus will return. And why need you lie to please me? I can see for myself that you are old and unhappy, a wanderer whom the Gods have sent to me. It is not for such a tale I will show you the kindness that you need, but because I pity you myself, and reverence the law of Zeus."

"If I lie," Odysseus answered, "you may have

me thrown from the cliff as a warning to other cheats. I swear it, and call the Gods to witness."

But the true-hearted swineherd only said, " I should get a good name by that, my friend, if I took you into my house and had you for my guest, and then murdered you brutally! Do you think I could pray to Zeus after that without a fear? But now it is supper-time, and my men will be coming home."

While they spoke, the herdsmen came up with the swine, and the sows were drawn into the pens, grunting and squealing noisily as they settled in for the night. Then Eumaeus called out, " Bring in the fattest boar, and let us make a sacrifice in honour of our guest, and get some reward ourselves for all the trouble we have spent upon the drove, trouble lost, since strangers take the fruit of it all."

So they brought in a big fat white-tusked boar, while Eumaeus split the wood for the fire. And he did not forget the Immortals, for he had a pious heart: he made the due offerings first and prayed for his master's return, and then he stood up at the board to carve, and gave each man his share, and a special slice for his guest from the whole length of the chine. Odysseus took it, and thanked him with all his heart:

" May Father Zeus be your friend, Eumaeus, and give you what I would give you for your kindness to a poor old man like me."

But the swineherd said, " Take it, my good friend,

take it and enjoy it. Zeus will give or withhold as it may please him, for he can do all things."

So they sat down to the feast, and after they had had their fill the swineherd's servant cleared everything away, and then they made ready for sleep. The evening closed in black and stormy, and a west wind sprang up bringing the rain with it, and blew hard all the night: so Eumaeus made up a bed of fleeces for Odysseus by the fire and gave him a great thick cloak as well, that he kept for the roughest weather. But he could not bring himself to stay there too, away from his herd of pigs, and he wrapped himself up warmly and went out to sleep beside them in the open. Odysseus saw, and smiled to see, what care he took of everything, while he thought his master was far away.

CHAPTER XV

HOW TELEMACHUS CAME HOME AGAIN

MEANWHILE Athena had gone to the palace of Menelaus, where it stood among the wide lawns of Sparta, to bid Telemachus start on his way home. His bed was laid in the palace-porch; but he could not sleep and lay there awake, thinking of his father all through the quiet night. Athena stood beside him, and said:

" Telemachus, it is not wise for you to be so long away from home. You have left behind you dangerous men who may rob you of all you have; and your mother is hard pressed by her father and her kin to marry Eurymachus, for he offers her more splendid gifts than all the other lords. If she listens to him she may soon forget the husband of her youth: a woman's mind is weak. But you must be on your guard as you go home: for the wooers are lying in wait for you in the strait between Ithaca and Samos. Keep your ship away from the islands, and sail by night as well as by day; and one of the deathless Gods who loves you will send you a fair breeze. And when you have reached Ithaca, send your ship and

E 10

your men to the city, but go yourself alone to the house of the swineherd Eumaeus."

So Athena went back to Olympus; and as soon as morning was come Telemachus said to Menelaus, "Send me on my way home to-day, O son of Atreus! for I long to see Ithaca once more." And Menelaus answered, "I will not keep you here, if you are longing for your home; but first I must give you a parting gift."

So he brought from his treasure chamber a cup and a silver bowl, and gave them to Telemachus; and Helen brought a wonderful robe of her own work, which shone like a star, and gave it to him and said, "Take this, dear child, in memory of Helen, and give it to your bride to wear upon her marriage-day; and may joy follow you to your home."

Then Telemachus and the son of Nestor yoked the horses, and drove the car out of the echoing courtyard; and Menelaus stood by the horses' heads and bade farewell to the youths, saying, "Farewell, and greet Nestor in my name: he was kind as a father to me, when we fought with the heroes at Troy." But Telemachus thought of his own father and said, "O that when I reach Ithaca I might find Odysseus at home, and tell him of all the kindness you have shown me!"

Even as he spoke an eagle flew across in front of them with a tame goose in its claws; and the son of Nestor said, "That is a sign sent by the Gods: tell us, Menelaus, what it means." Menelaus stood in doubt, but Helen said at once, "Listen to me, and I will tell you. Just as that eagle came from its home in the mountains and snatched the goose from the courtyard, so shall Odysseus return home after his long wanderings, and take vengeance on his foes."

Then Telemachus and Nestor's son drove away across the plain, till the sun went down and all the roads grew dark, and on the second day they came to sandy Pylos. The ship was waiting for them, and they bade farewell to one another, and Telemachus said they would be friends for ever, as their fathers had been before them.

And just as he was about to embark a man hurried up to the ship. Theoclymenus was his name, and he came of a race that had the gift of second-sight. He told Telemachus his story, how he had slain a man in his own country and was now an outlaw, and he begged that he might be taken on board; and Telemachus said to him, "Come with me, if you will, and you shall be welcome in Ithaca to all that I can give you."

So they went on board, and Athena sent them a fair wind, and the ship ran on over the wine-dark sea. They were careful not to pass by Samos, and so they escaped the suitors, and early next morning they came to the coast of Ithaca.

Then Telemachus said to the stranger, "In better days I would have bid you to our own house, but now you would get a poor welcome there; for my mother sits apart in her own chamber and seldom shows herself, and Eurymachus is master."

Then he told the crew that he wished to land before they reached the city, and he asked one of his friends to give Theoclymenus entertainment while he was away. So the ship put in to shore, and Telemachus landed; and the rest sailed round to the city, while he went alone across the country till he reached the swineherd's hut.

CHAPTER XVI

HOW ODYSSEUS MET HIS SON AGAIN

Now Odysseus and the swineherd were already preparing their breakfast when Telemachus came up. The dogs knew him and played round him lovingly. " Eumaeus," said Odysseus, " some friend of yours is coming, for I hear footsteps, and the dogs are pleased and do not bark."

He had hardly finished speaking, when his own dear son stood in the doorway. The swineherd started up and dropped the vessel in which he was mixing the wine. He went to meet his young master, and fell on his neck and kissed him as a father would kiss an only son escaped from death. " Light of my eyes, dear child, have you come home at last? When you sailed away to Pylos, I never thought to see you again. But come in and let me feast my eyes upon you; you do not often visit us, for you are kept at home in the town, watching that crowd of ruinous lords."

And Telemachus answered, " As you will, good father: indeed I have come to see you, and to hear tidings of my mother."

Then the swineherd told him that his mother still

waited patiently at home, and spent her days and nights in weeping.

Then Telemachus went into the house, and as he came up Odysseus rose to give him his seat, but he would not take it and said, " Keep your seat, stranger; this man shall make up another for me." So Odysseus sat down again, and the swineherd made a seat for Telemachus of the green brushwood and put a fleece upon it. Then he set food before them, and when they had eaten, Telemachus asked who the stranger was and how he had come to Ithaca. And Eumaeus told him Odysseus' own story and begged him to protect the wanderer. But Telemachus thought of the suitors and did not wish to take him to the palace.

" I will give him a cloak and a doublet," he said, " and shoes for his feet, and a two-edged sword, and I will send him on his way. But I cannot take him into the house, where the suitors would mock at him and use him ill. One man cannot restrain them, and he so young as I."

Then Odysseus said, " Sir, if I may speak, I would say foul wrong is done you in your house, and my heart burns at the thought. Do your people hate you, or will your brothers give you no support? Would that I were as young as you, and were Odysseus' son, or Odysseus himself! I would go to the palace and fall upon the throng, and die there, one man against a hundred, sooner than see the shameful deeds that are done in that glorious house."

And Telemachus answered, " Hear me, stranger, and I will tell you all. My people do not hate me, and I have no quarrel with them. But I have no brothers to stand by me, for Zeus has never given more than one son to each generation of our line. And there are many foemen in the house, all the princes of the islands, and they woo my mother and threaten my life, and I cannot see how it will end."

Then he said to Eumaeus, " Go up to the house, old father, as quickly as you can, and tell my mother that I am come back safe from Pylos; and I will wait for you here."

And Eumaeus answered, " I hear, master, and understand. But shall I not go to Laertes on my way, and tell him too? For, since you set sail for Pylos, they say he has not eaten or drunk or gone about his work, but sits in his house sorrowing and wasting away with grief."

But Telemachus bade him go straight to the palace and return at once, and let the queen send word to Laertes by one of the maids. So Eumaeus went forth, and when Athena saw him go, she drew near and came and stood by the gateway, and showed herself to Odysseus, a tall and beautiful woman, with wisdom in her look. The dogs saw her too and were afraid, and shrank away whining into the corner of the yard; but Telemachus could not see her. Then the Goddess signed to Odysseus, and he went out and stood before her, and she said, " Noble Odysseus, now is the time to make yourself known to your son and go forth with him to the town, with death and doom for the suitors. I shall be near you in the battle, and eager to fight."

Then she touched him with her golden wand, and gave him his beauty and stature once more, and his bronzed colour came back, and his beard grew thick and his garments shone bright again: and so she sent him to the hut. And when Telemachus saw him, he marvelled and turned away his eyes, for he thought it must be a God.

"Stranger," he said, "you have changed in a moment: your colour is not the same nor your garments. If you are one of the Immortals, be gracious to us, and let us offer you gifts and sacrifice."

Then Odysseus cried out, "I am no God, but your own dear father, for whose sake you are suffering cruel wrongs and the spite of men." And then he kissed his son and let his tears take their way at last.

But Telemachus could not believe it, and said, "You cannot be my father, but a God come down to deceive me and make me grieve still more. No mortal could do what you have done, for a moment since you were old and wretched and poorly clad, and now you seem like one of the heavenly Gods."

Then his father answered, "My son, no other Odysseus will ever come back to you. Athena has done this wonder, for she is a Goddess and can make men what she will, now poor, now rich, now old, now young: such power have the lords of heaven to exalt us or bring us low."

Then Telemachus fell on his neck and they wept aloud together. And they would have wept out their hearts till evening, had not Telemachus asked his father how he had come to Ithaca; and Odysseus told him that the Sea-kings had brought him, and put him on shore asleep, and that Athena had sent him to the swineherd's hut. " But now tell me of the suitors. How many are they? And what manner of men? Can the two of us make head against the throng? "

" Father," he answered, " I know well your fame, mighty and wise in war. But this we could never dare, two men against a host. They are a hundred and twenty in all, the best fighting men from Ithaca and the islands round. Think, if you can, of some champion who would befriend us and give us help."

And Odysseus made answer, " What think you, if Father Zeus and the Goddess Athena stood by our side? Should we still need other help? "

" Truly they are the best of champions," said Telemachus, " though they sit on high among the clouds; and they rule both men and Gods."

" And they will be with us," said his father," when we come to the trial of war. Now at daybreak you must go home and mix with the suitors, and later on the swineherd will bring me to the town, disguised again as the old beggar-man; and if they ill-treat me, or even strike me, or drag me out of the house, you must look on and bear it. You may check them by speaking, but they will not listen, for the

*E

day of their doom is at hand. And tell no one that Odysseus has come home, not even Laertes, nor the swineherd, nor Penelope herself: we must keep the secret until we are sure of our friends."

Then Telemachus said that his father might trust him, and so they talked on together. Meanwhile Eumaeus had reached the palace with the tidings that Telemachus had returned; and the suitors who were in the hall heard it and were dismayed, for they saw that their plot had been foiled. They went out of the palace and sat down before the gates, and were talking of sending word to their ship that was lying in wait for Telemachus, when the ship itself came into the harbour, with the other princes on board. So they all went up together to the public square and debated what to do, and they resolved to murder Telemachus as soon as they found another chance. Then they went back and sat down again on the polished seats in the hall.

Now Medon the herald had heard them plotting together in the square, and went and told Penelope all that they had said, and how they had purposed putting her son to death. She went down at once with her women, and stood in the doorway of the hall with her bright veil before her face, and spoke to Antinous and said, " Wicked and insolent man, can it be that they call you in Ithaca one of their wisest men? No. it is a fool's work you are doing, plotting to kill my son. He is helpless before you now, but Zeus is the friend of the helpless, and will avenge their wrongs.

Impious and ungrateful too! Did not Odysseus once shield your father from his enemies and save his life? Yet you waste his substance and would murder his son!"

Then Eurymachus spoke and tried to soothe her. No one, he said, should injure Telemachus while he was alive, for he loved him more than any man on earth. Eurymachus' words were fair, and Penelope could say no more; yet all the while he was planning the death of her son.

In the evening the swineherd reached his hut again, and found Odysseus changed to the old beggar-man once more, preparing supper with Telemachus.

"What tidings, good Eumaeus?" said the young man. "Have the proud lords come home from their ambush, or are they still waiting out yonder to take me as I return?"

And Eumaeus replied, "I did not stay, master, to go through the town and find out the news, for when I had given my message I wanted to be at home. But one thing I saw from the brow of the hill as I came along. A swift ship was entering the harbour, with armed men on board. They may have been the princes, but I cannot say."

As he heard this, Telemachus looked at his father and smiled, but he took good care that the swine-herd should not see.

CHAPTER XVII

HOW ODYSSEUS CAME TO THE PALACE

EARLY next morning, when the rosy-fingered dawn was in the sky, Telemachus bound on his sandals and took his stout spear in his hand, and said to the swineherd, " Old friend, I must now be off to the city and let my mother see me, for I know she will weep and mourn until I am there myself. And as for this poor stranger, I would have you take him to the town, and let him beg for bite and sup from door to door, and those who choose can give. For I cannot be host to every wanderer, with all the trouble I have to bear. And if that makes him angry —well! it is only the worse for him: I am a man who speaks his mind."

Then Odysseus answered readily, " Sir, I do not ask to stay here myself: a beggar should not beg in the fields. Nor am I young enough to work on a farm at a master's beck and call. So go your ways, and your man shall take me with him to the town. But I will wait till the sun is high, for I am afraid of the morning-frost with these threadbare rags of mine."

So Telemachus strode away until he reached the palace, and there he went into the hall. The old nurse Eurycleia was up already with the maids, spreading fleeces on the inlaid stools and chairs; and she saw him at once and went to him with tears in her eyes, and then all the women gathered round and kissed him and welcomed him home again. And Penelope came down from her chamber, and flung her arms round her son, and kissed his head and both his eyes, and said to him tearfully, "You have come home, Telemachus, light of my eyes! I thought I should never see you again, when you sailed away to Pylos secretly, against my will, to get tidings of your father. And now tell me all you heard."

But Telemachus said to her, "Mother, why make me think of trouble now, when I have just escaped from death? Rather put on your fairest robes, and go and pray the Gods to grant us a day of vengeance. But I must be off to the public square to meet a guest of mine whom I brought here in my ship. I sent him on before me with the crew, and bade one of them take him to his house until I came myself."

So Penelope went away and prayed to the Gods, while the prince went down to the public square and found Theoclymenus, and brought him back to the palace, and they sat down together in the hall. Then one of the old servants brought up a polished table and spread it for them with good things for their meal, and Penelope came and sat beside the door, spinning her fine soft yarn. She did not speak till they had finished, but then she said to her son, "Telemachus, I see I must go up to my room and lie down on my bed, the bed I have watered with

my tears ever since Odysseus went away to Troy; for you are determined not to talk to me and tell me the news of your father before the suitors come into the hall."

Then Telemachus said, "Mother, I will tell you all I know. We reached Pylos and found Nestor there, and he took me into his splendid house, and welcomed me as lovingly as though I had been a long-lost son of his own. But he could tell me nothing of my father, not even if he were alive or dead, and so he sent me on to Sparta, to the house of Menelaus. There I saw Helen, the fairest of women, for whom the Greeks and Trojans fought and suffered so long. Menelaus asked me why I came, and I told him about the suitors, and all the wrong they did. Then he cried: ' Curse on them! The dastards in the hero's place! O that Odysseus would return! They would soon have cause enough to hate this suit of theirs!' And then he told me how he had heard tidings of my father from Proteus, the wizard of the sea. He was living still, so the wizard said, on an island far away, in the cave of a wood-nymph called Calypso, who kept him there against his will, and he had no ship to carry him over the broad sea. That was all Menelaus could tell me; and when I had done my errand I came away, and the Gods have brought me home in safety."

And as Penelope listened her heart filled with sorrow; but Theoclymenus, the seer, said to her, " Listen to me, wife of Odysseus, and I will prophesy to you; for your son has heard nothing certain, but I have seen omens that are sure. I swear by Zeus, the ruler of the Gods, and by the board and the hearth of Odysseus himself, where I am standing now—he is already here in Ithaca, he knows of all this wickedness, and is waiting to punish the suitors as they deserve."

At that moment the princes came in from their sport, and flung their cloaks aside, and set about slaughtering the sheep and the fatted goats and the swine for their feast.

Meanwhile Odysseus was starting for the town, with the swineherd to show him the way. He had slung the tattered wallet across his shoulder, and Eumaeus had given him a staff, and everyone who met them would have taken the king for a poor old beggarman, hobbling along with his crutch.

So they went down the rocky path till they reached a running spring by the wayside where the townsfolk got their water. There was a grove of tall poplars round it, and the cool stream bubbled down from the rock overhead, and above the fountain there was an altar to the nymphs where the passersby laid their offerings.

There they chanced to meet Melanthius, the king's goatherd, driving his fattest goats to the town for the suitors' feast. He was a favourite of theirs, and did all he could to please them. Now as soon as he saw the two he broke out into scoffs and gibes, till the heart of Odysseus grew hot with anger.

"Look there!" he shouted, "one rascal leading another! Trust a man to find his mate! A plague on you, swineherd, where are you taking that pitiful wretch? Another beggar, I suppose, to hang about the doors and cringe for the scraps and spoil our feasts? Now, if you would only let me have him to watch my farm and sweep out my stalls and fetch fodder for my kids, he could drink as much whey as he liked and get some flesh on his bones. But no! His tricks have spoilt him for any honest work!"

So he jeered at them in his folly, and as he passed he kicked Odysseus on the thigh; but the king stood firm, and took the blow in silence, though he could have found it in his heart to strike the man dead on the spot. But Eumaeus turned round fiercely, and cried to the Gods for vengeance:

"Nymphs of the spring," he prayed, "if ever my master honoured you, hear my prayer, and send him home again! He would make a sweep of all your insolence, you good-for-nothing wretch, loitering here in the city while your flocks are left to ruin!"

"Oho!" cried Melanthius, "listen to the foul-mouthed dog! I must put him on board a ship and sell him in a foreign land, and make some use of him that way! Why, Odysseus will never see the day of his return! He is dead and gone: I wish his son would follow him!"

With that he turned on his heel and hastened away to the palace-hall, where he sat down with the suitors at their feast. And the other two followed slowly until they reached the gate. There they paused, and Odysseus caught the swineherd by the hand, and cried:

"Eumaeus, this must be the palace of the king!

No one could mistake it. See, there is room after room, and a spacious court-yard with a wall and coping-stones, and solid double doors to make all safe. And I am sure that a great company is seated there at the banquet, for I can smell the roasted meat and hear the sound of the lyre."

Then Eumaeus said, " Your wits are quick enough; it is the very place. And now tell me: would you rather go in alone, and face the princes while I wait here, or will you stay behind and let me go in first? Only, if you wait here, you must not wait too long, for someone might catch sight of you and strike you and drive you from the gate."

Then the hero said to him, " I understand; I knew what I had to meet. Do you go first, and I will wait behind. For I have some knowledge of thrusts and blows, and my heart has learned to endure; for I have suffered much in storm and battle, and can bear this like the rest."

But while they were talking, a dog who was lying at the gate lifted his head and pricked up his ears. It was the hound Argus whom Odysseus had reared himself long ago before the war, but he had to leave him behind when he went away to Troy. Once he used to follow the hunters to the chase, but no one cared for him now when his master was away, and he lay there covered with vermin, on a dung-heap in front of the gates. Yet even so, when he felt that Odysseus was near him, he wagged his tail and dropped his ears; but he had not strength enough to drag himself up to his master. And when Odysseus saw it, he turned away his face so that Eumaeus should not see the tears in his eyes, and said, "Eumaeus, it is strange that they let that dog lie there in the dung. He looks a noble creature, but perhaps he has never been swift enough for the chase, and they have only kept him for his beauty."

"Ah, yes!" Eumaeus answered, "it is easy to see that he has no master now. If you had been here when Odysseus went to Troy, you would have wondered at the creature's pace and strength. In the thickest forest no quarry could escape him, and no hound had ever keener scent. But now he is old and wretched, and his lord has perished far away, and the heedless women take no care of him. Slaves can do nothing as they ought when their master is not there, for a man loses half his manhood when he falls into slavery."

Then Eumaeus went on into the palace and up to the hall among the suitors. But Argus had seen his master again at last, and when he had seen him, he died.

As soon as the swineherd came in, Telemachus caught sight of him, and beckoned him to a stool at his side, and gave him his share of the feast. After a little while Odysseus came up too, and sat down on the threshold like a poor old beggarman. Then his son sent him meat and bread by the swineherd, and said that a beggar should be bold, and he ought

to go among the princes and ask each man for a
dole.   So he went round from one to the other,
stretching out his hand for a morsel in the true
beggar's way.   And everyone else felt some pity and
gave him an alms, but Antinous mocked at them all,
and told them they were ready enough to be gener-
ous with another's wealth.   And at last he grew
angry and cursed Odysseus for a whining rascal,
and hurled a footstool at his head, bidding him be-
gone and trouble them no more.   The stool struck
Odysseus on the shoulder, but he stood like a rock,
motionless and silent, with black thoughts in his
heart.   Then he went back straight to the threshold:
and sat down and spoke to all the company:

" Listen to me, my lords!   No man bears any
rancour for a blow in open war, but Antinous has
struck me because I am a beggar and know the
curse of hunger.   If there be any Gods who avenge
the poor man's cause, I pray that he may die before
his marriage-day!"

At that the others felt shame, and told Antinous
he did wrong to strike the homeless wanderer.

"Who knows?" they said.   " He might be one of
the heavenly Gods, and woe to you if he were!   For
sometimes the Immortals take upon themselves the
likeness of strangers, and enter our cities, and go
about among men, watching the good and evil that
they do."

Thus they warned him, but he cared little for all
they said.   And Telemachus sat there full of rage

and grief to see his father **struck**, but he kept back the tears and held his peace.

Now Penelope was sitting in her room behind the hall, and she saw what had happened, and was angry with Antinous and called the swineherd to her side:

" Go, good Eumaeus, and tell the stranger to come here.   And I will ask him if he has ever heard of Odysseus, for he looks like a man who has wandered far."

And the swineherd said, " Yes, he is a Cretan, and has had all kinds of adventures before he was driven here, and he could tell you stories that would charm you like the minstrel's sweetest song, and you would never tire of listening.   And he says that he has heard of Odysseus, near home, in the rich land of Epirus, and that he is already on his way to us, bringing a store of treasures with him."

Then Penelope said, " Quick, bring the stranger here at once, and let him speak with me face to face! And if I see that he tells me the truth I will give him a doublet and a cloak for himself."

So the swineherd hurried back with the message; but Odysseus said he dared not face the princes a second time, and it would be better to speak with Penelope later in the evening, alone by the fire-side; and when the queen heard this, she said that the stranger was right.   By this time it was afternoon, and Eumaeus went up to Telemachus and whispered that he must be off to his work again.   Telemachus said he might go, but bade him have food first, and told him to come back next morning without fail. So the swineherd took his meal in the hall, and then started home for his farm, to look after his pigs and everything that he had charge of there.

CHAPTER XVIII

HOW ODYSSEUS FOUGHT WITH THE BEGGAR

THEN a common beggar came up to the doors, a rascal who was known through all the island for his endless eating and drinking. His name was Irus, and he used to run errands for the young lords: he was big enough to look at, but he had no strength or spirit in him. Up he came and called insolently to Odysseus, "Back from the doorway, old man! Else I will drag you out by the heels, though I am half ashamed to fight with such as you."

The king eyed him askance, and said, "My friend, I have done you no harm, and this threshold has room for us both. Do not provoke me too far, or, old as I am, I will let you feel how I can strike. Then we should have more peace to-morrow: for I reckon you would not come back a second time to the hall of King Odysseus."

"Listen to the glutton!" cried Irus. "How he gabbles on like an old wife over the fire! I will have at him right and left, and knock all the teeth from his jaws. Strip yourself, fellow, and let these lords see us fight."

Antinous heard them wrangling, and laughed out loud. " Friends, here is the best sport the Gods have ever sent this way! Irus and the stranger are challeng- ing one another! Come, let us make a ring." Then all the princes leapt up laughing, and gathered round the ragged beggars, and Antinous said again, " Look, there are the pies, which were put aside for supper, lying by the fire. Whichever shows himself the better man shall take his pick of them, and he shall dine with us every day, and we will let no one else come here to ask for alms."

Then Odysseus said craftily, " Sirs, an old man worn with trouble is no match for a younger man, but my hunger drives me to face the fight. Only I ask you all to swear that none of you will help Irus, or strike me an unfair blow."

They all swore as he asked, and Telemachus said, " Stranger, if you can meet this fellow you need fear no other man. Whoever strikes you will have to reckon with more than one: for I am your host, and Antinous and Eurymachus will help to see fair play."

When Odysseus heard that, he girded up his rags, till all could see his stalwart thighs and broad shoulders and strong arms: so that the princes stood amazed and said to one another, " What thighs the old man has under his rags! There will be little left of Irus when this fight is done." Irus trembled in every limb, but there was no help for it: the servants girded him and dragged him into the ring. At first Odysseus meant to strike him dead on the spot; but when he thought again he judged it better not to use all his strength, for fear the suitors should discover who he was. So the two put up their hands, and at the first blow Odysseus smote Irus on the neck, below the ear, and crushed in the bones, and he fell moaning in the dust: while all the princes laughed till they could laugh no more.

Odysseus took the fallen man by the foot and dragged him into the court-yard: there he set him up against a wall with his staff in his hands, and said, "Sit here, and scare away the swine, but do not try again to lord it over strangers, or a worse thing will happen to you." Then he went back to the hall and sat down again in his place on the threshold.

They all shouted as he came in, and said, "May Zeus give you your heart's desire, stranger, for ridding us of that hungry beggar!" And Odysseus rejoiced at the good omen of their words. Then Antinous set a great pasty before him, and another of the lords, called Amphinomus, brought him bread, and pledged him in a golden cup and wished him happiness. Now Amphinomus was good at heart, and Odysseus knew it, and tried to warn him. "Let me tell you," he said, "what is in my thoughts. There is no creature upon earth frailer than man: he is what the will of Heaven makes him: and yet, so long as all is well with him and he can feel his strength, he thinks that he can never come to harm.

So it was with me in former days: I trusted in my wealth and my kindred, and in the pride of my strength I did many lawless deeds. And so it is now with these princes. I see them plundering the wealth and dishonouring the wife of a man whom they never think to see again: and yet he is not so far away. Heaven grant that you may not meet him at his return! Go to your house in time: for he will not part from the suitors without bloodshed, when once he is within these walls."

With that he drank, and gave back the cup to the youth, who went sadly through the hall, shaking his head and foreboding ill: yet for all that his fate found him there.

Meanwhile it came into the heart of Penelope to show herself to the wooers. She laughed a joyless laugh, and said to one of her women who stood near, "I have a wish that I never had before, to let my wooers see me, though I hate them with all my heart. Go and bid two of my maidens come and attend me in the hall, for I cannot go alone among the men."

So the old woman went away to take the message, and meanwhile Athena sent a deep slumber on the queen. Her head fell back upon the pillow and her whole frame sank to rest: and then the Goddess gave her wonderful gifts, so that her face grew beautiful with the beauty of the Immortals, and she seemed taller than before and whiter than fresh-cut ivory. Now while she slept her attendants came up from the hall, and at the sound of their voices she awoke, and rubbed her eyes and said, "What a soft sleep has come over me in the midst of my troubles! O, for a death as gentle, to take me from this weary life of longing for my dear husband who is lost!"

Then she went down with her attendants to the hall, and stood by the doorway, holding her veil before her face; and all the wooers wondered at her beauty, and each of them longed to win her for himself. And Eurymachus said to her, "Daughter of Icarius, if all the Greeks could see you now, there would be still more suitors in your hall, for in wisdom and loveliness you surpass all other women."

But she answered, "Eurymachus, the Immortals took away all my beauty the day the Greeks embarked for Troy, and my husband Odysseus with them. I remember how he laid his hand upon my wrist when we parted, and said, 'Wife, many of us will never come home again. There are good warriors in Troy, men say, horsemen and spearmen and archers: and what will be my fate I cannot tell. So I leave everything in your charge, and you must not forget my father and mother, but take more care of them than ever while I am away. But when my son is grown to manhood, you may leave this house and marry whom you please.' And now it is all happening as he said. The black day will come when I must meet this marriage that I hate. But I am ill pleased at the way in which my wooers treat me. It was the custom once for men who wooed a king's daughter to give her splendid gifts, and make a feast for her friends, instead of devouring wealth that was not theirs."

So she spoke, and Odysseus smiled to himself, as he saw how she drew the suitors on, while her heart was far from them.

Then Antinous made answer, "Take our gifts, daughter of Icarius: it is right that we should bring them. But here we mean to stay until you have married the best man among us." And all the rest agreed, and the heralds fetched the gifts that every man would give: an embroidered robe with twelve golden clasps, and a golden necklace set with amber beads, and bracelets, and glittering earrings, and many another splendid gift. So Penelope went back to her chamber, and the maidens followed carrying the gifts; while the princes sang and danced and made merry until evening came.

When it grew dark the maids brought in great braziers full of dry billets, and set light to them, and stood round to keep the fires burning. Then the king went up to his servants, and said, "Servants of Odysseus, go back to your mistress, and sit beside her to cheer her with your company; and I will watch the fires for these guests. If they choose to see the dawn come up, they will not tire me: I am a man who has gone through much."

The girls looked at one another and laughed, and Melantho, the fairest and most shameless of them all, said to him scornfully, "Are you out of your wits, stranger? You should be off to sleep in the smithy or in the market-place: but here you stop and will be talking. I suppose your head is turned because you have beaten Irus. Wait till a better man than Irus comes to drive you out of doors."

But Odysseus looked at her sternly under his brows, and said, "Vixen, I will tell the prince Telemachus what you say, and he will cut you limb from limb." That scared the women, and they went trembling from the hall; and Odysseus remained, standing by the braziers, watching the feasters, and brooding all the while on the vengeance which was to come.

But it was not yet time for Athena to end his humiliation, and she let the suitors insult him at their will. First Eurymachus began to mock him, that he might make the others laugh. "The Gods," he said, "must have sent this stranger to be our torch-bearer: his head might serve to give us light, it is so bald and shining." Then he went on, turning to Odysseus: "Would you be ready to work for me, if I hired you, to build walls and plant trees on a distant farm of mine? I would pay you a good wage, and give you food and clothes. But you have learnt too many tricks for that: you would rather go begging through the country and gorge yourself all day long."

Then the hero answered him: "Eurymachus, it would please me well if we two could have a match at reaping, in the spring season when the days are long. There should be a meadow deep in grass, and a stout sickle for me and one for you, and we would work without food till sundown. Or there should be a pair of oxen for us to drive, great tawny beasts, and four acres of land to plough, and a soil that would give before the ploughshare: you would see then if I could cut a furrow straight. Or I could wish that an enemy might come down on us this very day, and that I had a shield, and two spears, and a helmet all of bronze set close upon my temples: you would see me among the foremost fighters, and have no cause to mock my hunger then. But you are insolent and have no mercy: you think that you are someone great and strong, because the men about you are few and weak. I tell you, if Odysseus were to come to his home again, these doors, broad as they are, would be all too narrow for your flight."

That made Eurymachus beside himself with rage, and he seized a footstool and hurled it: but Odysseus slipped aside, and the stool struck the cupbearer on the hand and felled him to the ground. Then there was a clamour in the hall and the princes cried, "Curse the vagabond! Why did he come here to trouble us? Now we sit wrangling over beggars, and everything goes wrong, and we get no pleasure out of this good feast."

Then Telemachus spoke out boldly: "Sirs, you cannot carry your wine in peace. I will not drive any

man away; but my counsel is that you make an end
of the feast, and go home now for the night." And
Amphinomus said that he had spoken well, and bade
the herald close the feast; so they drank the last cup
and went away, each man to his own house.

CHAPTER XIX

HOW ODYSSEUS WAS RECOGNISED BY THE OLD NURSE

THUS Odysseus and his son were left alone in the hall. Then Odysseus said, " We must put away all the weapons. If the suitors miss them and ask the reason, you can say you have laid them aside to keep them from the smoke."

So Telemachus called out the old nurse Eurycleia from the room behind the hall, and said to her, " Nurse, keep the women in their chambers while I stow away my father's weapons. They have been left here too long, and are tarnished by the smoke." " Yes, my child," said Eurycleia, " and I wish that you would always show such care for what belongs to you. But tell me, who is to carry the light for you, if you will not let the women come? " And Telemachus said that the stranger would carry it.

So the old woman shut the inner doors of the hall. Then Odysseus and his son sprang up and carried out the helmets and shields and spears: and Pallas Athena went before them with a golden lamp in her hand, and shed a wonderful light around them.

Telemachus turned to his father in amazement: "Father, what strange sight is this? The walls and the pillars and the pinewood rafters are all glowing as though they were lit up with fire. Surely one of the Gods who rule in heaven is with us here."

But the wise Odysseus answered: "Hold your peace, and keep the vision in your heart, and ask no questions. This is the way of the Immortals. And now you must go and sleep; but I will wait here, for I must speak to your mother and the women."

So Telemachus went to his own room, and Odysseus was left alone. And presently Penelope came out of her chamber, fair as an Immortal. Her women set her seat in its place by the hearth, a throne of ivory and silver with a footstool for her feet: and the maidservants cleared away the tables and piled fresh logs upon the fire. Then Penelope made them put a stool for Odysseus at her side and lay a fleece upon it. So he took his seat, and she began: "Stranger, tell me first who you are, and whence you come."

And Odysseus answered warily: "Lady, there is none in the wide world who would not praise you. Your fame is spread abroad like that of a just and mighty king, whose land is fruitful and whose people prosper beneath his rule. Ask no questions about my own country, for the thought of it would bring more sorrow to my heart: I am a man of many troubles, and it is not right that I should sit weeping and lamenting in another's house."

"Ah! stranger," said Penelope, "all my beauty and dignity left me the day when my husband Odysseus sailed for Troy. Since then I have forgotten the claims of guests, and waste my heart in longing for him. Meanwhile all the princes of Ithaca and the islands round make their suit to me, though it is much against my will. For a time I put them off by cunning, but now I cannot think of any way to escape: my father and mother would have me marry, and my son, now that he is grown a man, is vexed to see the ruin of his wealth. But, I pray you, tell me of yourself and your own people."

Then Odysseus began a story, so cunning that it sounded true. He said that his home was in the rich island of Crete, and he told of its inhabitants and its cities, and spoke of his own father and family, and said he had once entertained Odysseus, when a storm had driven him to their shore. Penelope listened, and her tears began to fall, like snow that melts on the mountains at the breath of the first warm wind. So she wept for her own husband, who was sitting by her side. Pity filled the heart of Odysseus, but he forced back the tears and set his eyes like steel. And when his wife had wept out her heart, she spoke to him again: "Now, stranger, I will put you to the test, and see whether you did in truth entertain my husband as you say. Tell me what were the clothes he wore, and how he looked, and who were his companions."

"Lady," said Odysseus, "it is not easy to say

after so long a time, for it is twenty years by now since he left my country; but I will tell you how my mind remembers him. He wore a thick purple mantle with a brooch of gold, and on the face of the brooch was wrought a hound that held in its grip a dappled fawn. I remember too his doublet, how smooth and glossy it was; and there was a herald in his company, a little older than he; he was round-shouldered and dark-skinned and curly-haired, and Odysseus honoured him more than all his fellows."

At that Penelope sobbed again, and said, "Stranger, I pitied you from the first, but now I shall love and honour you. It was I myself who gave him those garments and fastened the glittering brooch. But I shall never welcome him home again. It was under an evil doom that he sailed from here to that hateful town of Troy."

And Odysseus answered, "Noble lady, do not waste your heart with weeping; for I heard tidings of Odysseus but latterly, when I was in the land of Epirus. He has lost all his comrades, it is true, and his ship is sunk in the dark sea; for the Gods were angry with him. But he himself is safe, and not far off: I swear to you that he will come home in this very year, yes, before the next moon is full."

"Ah! stranger," said Penelope, "my heart misgives me that he will never come home again, nor entertain you here as he would wish. But now my maids shall wash your feet, and make a bed for you here; and to-morrow you shall sit by Telemachus at the feast, and none of the princes shall dare to touch you. How could you call me wise, if I let you sit uncared-for in my house?"

"Lady," answered Odysseus, "I have lain many a night on a hard bed, waiting for the bright dawn to rise, and so I will lie to-night. Nor do I wish that any of your maids should wash my feet: only if there is some old woman in the house, true of heart, who has borne such trouble as I have known myself, I would suffer her to touch me."

Then Penelope said, "Dear stranger, none of my guests have ever been as wise as you. There is a faithful old woman with me, who used to nurse my lord and carry him in her arms when he was a child: she shall wash your feet. Come here, good Eurycleia, and serve this man: he is your master's age, and Odysseus with all his trouble may look like him by now."

At her words the old woman covered her face with her hands, and wept, and said, "O my child Odysseus, my heart aches for you! There was never any man who honoured the Gods as he did; and yet they have not let him return. Perhaps he too is a beggar in some foreign house, and the women mock him there. Yes, stranger, I will do what Penelope bids me, and gladly, for my heart is drawn to you. And I tell you this, of all the guests who have ever come to this house, none has been so like Odysseus in step and face and voice."

And Odysseus said, "May-be, old mother: so men say who have seen us both."

Then she brought a basin and filled it with water. And as she did so, Odysseus turned quickly away from the firelight; for the thought came to him that

she might find the scar of an old wound where a wild boar had gashed him when he was a boy, and so the truth might be known. But she came up to him and began to wash his feet, and as she passed her hands down the leg she felt the scar, and knew it by the touch. She dropped his foot suddenly, and the bronze basin was overturned and rang on the ground, and all the water was spilt. Sorrow and joy came over her together, and her eyes filled with tears, and the voice died in her throat. Then she cried: " You are he, you are Odysseus! And I never knew you, my child, until I had touched you with my own hands!"

As she spoke she looked at Penelope, longing to tell her that her husband was at home. But Penelope did not see and did not notice, for Athena had turned her thoughts away. Then Odysseus put his hand on the old woman's mouth, and said, " Nurse, would you kill me? You carried me at your breast: and would you be my ruin, now that I have come home at last? Be silent, and let no one else in the house know what you have seen; or I swear I will have no mercy on you, my nurse though you are, when the day of reckoning comes."

" My child," answered Eurycleia, " why need you speak to me like that? You know the strength of my heart: I will be firm as iron."

" Be silent, then," said Odysseus, " and leave the rest to Heaven."

Then the old woman brought water in place of what was spilt, and washed her master's feet and anointed him. And when it was done Odysseus covered up the scar with his rags and drew the stool nearer to the fire. Then Penelope said to him, " Stranger, there is still one small thing I wish to ask you. I am all in doubt whether I should stay here with my son, or marry the best of these lords who woo me. And now I will tell you a dream that I have had, and you shall interpret it. I have twenty geese in the courtyard: they feed on wheat out of a trough, and it gladdens my heart to see them. Now in my dream I thought that a fierce eagle swooped from the mountains, and broke the necks of my geese and killed them: and I wept over them bitterly as they lay dead on the ground. But the eagle perched on a jutting beam, and spoke in a human voice: 'Daughter of Icarius, take courage: this is no dream, but a true vision of what shall come to pass. The geese are the wooers, and I, the eagle, I am your husband, come back to work vengeance on them all.' At his words sleep left me, and I looked up and saw my geese, picking the wheat by the trough as before."

And Odysseus answered her, " Lady, there is only one way to interpret the dream, for Odysseus himself has told you. This forebodes the death of all the suitors."

But Penelope said, " Dreams are things of doubtful meaning, and hard to understand. But now listen to what I have to say. To-morrow I will make my suitors show who is the best among them. They shall take the bow of Odysseus, and try to shoot an arrow through twelve pierced axes in a row,[1] as he used to do. And he who can do this feat shall be my husband and take me from this fair house, so full of treasures, the house to which I came as a bride, and which I shall remember in my dreams."

[1] See Note B at end.

Then Odysseus said at once: " Lady, let this trial be held without delay. Odysseus will be here before they can bend that bow."

Then Penelope bade her attendants prepare a couch for Odysseus, and she herself went to her own chamber and wept till she fell asleep.

CHAPTER XX

HOW ODYSSEUS SPENT HIS FIRST NIGHT AT HOME

ODYSSEUS lay down in the corridor outside the hall, but the anger burnt in his heart so that he could not rest; and he lay tossing from side to side, wondering how he should make head against his enemies, one against so many. Then Athena came down from heaven, and stood beside him in the likeness of a mortal woman, and said, "Cannot you rest at last, Odysseus? This is your own home, and your wife is here, and your son, a son after a hero's heart."

"That is true," replied Odysseus, "but I cannot tell how I shall do battle with these wooers, for I am one, and they a host. And, even if by Heaven's favour I should slay them, will there not be vengeance taken for their deaths?"

Then the grey-eyed Goddess answered, "O doubting heart! Other men can trust in their friends who are weak and mortal and know less than I. I am a Goddess, and I guard you constantly in all your perils: yes, though there were fifty companies of men about us, bent upon your death, you should overcome them all. Sleep therefore, since the end

*F

of your trouble is not far away." Then she went back to Olympus, and left Odysseus sleeping.

But Penelope's slumber was broken by sorrow, and she lay weeping for her husband, and calling on death to take her from her grief. And, as Odysseus woke at early dawn, her voice was in his ears, and it seemed to him as though she already knew him and was standing by his side. He sprang up, and went to the great altar in the courtyard, and lifted up his hands in prayer to Zeus: " Father Zeus, grant me a sign, so that I may know if it is thou indeed who hast led me over land and sea and brought me to my journey's end."

So he prayed, and Zeus heard him from heaven, and sent a peal of thunder. And a poor maidservant, who had been grinding meal for the household all night long, and was working still, heard the crash, and stopped the millstone she was turning, and said, " Thunder from a clear sky, and no cloud in sight! That must be a sign from heaven. Perhaps the Gods will listen even to one so weak as I. Those princes who feast in the house of Odysseus have made me grind for their banquet until my strength is broken. I pray that this meal may be their last."

And Odysseus rejoiced at the thunder-peal and the woman's words, for he knew that the day of vengeance was come.

Meanwhile the other maidservants had gathered in the hall, and were lighting the fire on the hearth. Presently Telemachus came out from his chamber,

with his spear in his hand and his sword slung about
him. He stopped at the threshold and said to Eurycleia, " Nurse, has the stranger been well cared-for?
Wise though my mother is, she does not always show
favour to those who deserve it most."

" You need not blame her in this, my child," said
Eurycleia. " The stranger drank wine to his heart's
content, but he would not taste food, for she asked
him. And though he slept on a rough bed outside
the hall, that was his own desire."

Then Telemachus went out to the city, with his
two dogs at his heels. Meanwhile Eurycleia and
the maids prepared the hall, and the serving-men
brought in the logs. Presently Eumaeus joined them,
driving three fat boars, the best in his herd. He let
them feed about the courtyard, and spoke to Odysseus, asking how the princes had treated him, and
Odysseus told him of their insolence. Then up came
Melanthius with his goats, and he began to taunt
Odysseus again, and tried to provoke him to a fight,
but Odysseus would not answer a word.

While they stood there, another herdsman came
up, driving a heifer before him: his name was
Philoetius, and he was a loyal man. He gazed at
Odysseus, and asked the swineherd who the stranger
was. " He has the look of a king, spite of his rags,"
he said, and he grasped Odysseus by the hand:
" Welcome, old father! May your troubles have a
happy end! The tears spring to my eyes when
I see you, for you put me in mind of my master

Odysseus, who gave me charge of the cattle when I was a little lad. And ever since then they have thriven and increased, till now you could not see a finer herd: but I can take no joy in them, for I must drive them here to be the food of strangers. Yes, and I would have left my home long ago and taken service with some other lord, for it is past all bearing: but I still think of my master in his troubles! It may be he will yet come home and drive out the usurpers."

"That is bravely spoken, shepherd," said Odysseus. "And now hear my answer. Wait a little, and I swear Odysseus will come home, and your own eyes shall see their fall."

While they spoke the princes came in from the town, and took their places at the feast. Telemachus made Odysseus come in too, and was careful to seat him just inside the door beside the great stone threshold: he gave him a mean stool and a little table, and brought him meat and drink, and said, "Sit down, and do not be afraid: I will have no brawling here, for this is the house of Odysseus, and the inheritance is mine."

"Let him talk," said Antinous to the other chiefs. "But if Zeus had not hindered us, we would have shut his mouth for good." Then one of them called out, "Your guest shall have his share, Telemachus: here is a gift for him from me"; and with that he caught up a marrow-bone from the basket and hurled it at Odysseus. But the king ducked and let it pass, smiling grimly to himself. "Well for you that you missed," said Telemachus to the other, "or I would have run you through the body with my spear! There would have been no wedding after that, but a funeral, at your father's house. Let us have an end of this: I am a boy no longer, and I will not bear it."

Then another of the suitors spoke, and said he was right to protect a stranger and a guest. "But you must listen, Telemachus, to what we have to say. As long as there was hope of your father's return, it was fair that you should delay our suit and keep us waiting here. But now it is plain that he will never come back. Go now, tell your mother that she must make her choice at last." "Let her marry whom she pleases," said Telemachus, "I will not stand in her way."

Then a strange madness came on them all, and they laughed and could not cease. And as they laughed, their faces changed, and the meat before them dripped with blood, and their eyes filled with tears, and sobs rose from the hearts of all. Then the seer Theoclymenus cried aloud, "Wretched men, what doom is come upon you? Your heads and your knees are wrapped in darkness, and your cheeks are wet with tears, and there goes up a cry of wailing, and the walls are stained with blood. Ghosts throng in the porch and in the courtyard, hurrying downwards to the land of death; and the sun is blotted out of heaven, and a dreary mist has overspread the world."

But they only laughed the more, and Eurymachus said, " The man is mad. Lead him out of the house to the market-place, since he finds it so dark in here."

" Eurymachus," said the seer, " I need no guides from you. I have eyes and ears, and I can understand. But I will go forth from this place, for I see a doom coming, and none of you shall escape who riot in the house of King Odysseus."

So he spoke and went forth from the palace. But the young lords taunted Telemachus: " You are unlucky in your guests," they said. " First you have a hungry wanderer, who cannot fight or work; and now this other fellow stands up and prophesies. Sell them for slaves: they are good for nothing else."

But Telemachus took no heed of what they said: he sat silent, looking towards his father and waiting till the time to act should come.

CHAPTER XXI

HOW THE SUITORS TRIED TO BEND THE BOW OF
ODYSSEUS, AND HOW ODYSSEUS SHOT AN ARROW
TO THE MARK

Now Penelope sat in the women's room behind the
inner doors,[1] listening to the laughter and the talk,
until it came into her heart to fetch the bow and let
the trial begin. She called her women, and went to
the treasury where the wealth of the king was stored,
wrought iron and bronze and gold. There hung the
quiver full of deadly arrows, and the great polished
bow which one of the heroes had given to Odysseus
in old days. Penelope took it from the peg, and drew
off its shining case; and she sat down and laid it
on her knees, and sobbed over it. Then she went to
meet the princes, and her attendants followed carrying the axes. She stood by the doorpost holding up
her veil before her face, and said:

"Listen to me, my lords. You have eaten and
drunk in my house all these years, while my husband
was away. You have called yourselves my suitors,
and that was your only plea. Now here is the
prize you ask for. I have brought the great bow of

[1] See Note A at end.

Odysseus, and I will give myself to the man who can bend it and shoot an arrow through twelve axes in a row."

Then she told Eumaeus to take it and set out the pierced axes for the suitors to try their skill.[1] Eumaeus shed tears as he took it, and the shepherd wept with him when he saw his master's bow. But Antinous said to them harshly, "Wretched boors, why do you whimper like cowards, and distress your lady, who has grief enough already? Hold your tongues and go and weep outside, and leave the bow to us. We shall have trouble enough before we bend it, for there is not a man among us all to match Odysseus. I saw him myself and remember him well, though I was then but a child." So he said, but all the while he believed that he could bend the bow himself.

Then Telemachus declared that he would try with the rest, and that if he won his mother need not leave her home. He stood up and dug a trench straight down the middle of the earthen floor, and planted the axes in it, one behind the other, and stamped the earth fast about them: and then he took up the bow. Three times he strained with all his force till it trembled under his hands, and three times he had to let it go. And at the fourth attempt he might have strung it, but Odysseus shook his head. That stopped him, and he cried, " I am still too young for such a feat! Come, now, those of you who are stronger than I, take the bow and end the match."

[1] See Note B at end.

Then Antinous said that they should all try in order as they sat, and that the priest, whose place was next the wine-bowl, should begin. So the priest stood up and went to the threshold, and took the bow: and he strained till his delicate hands grew weary, but he could not bend it at all. At last he laid it down, and said, " Friends, I can do nothing: let the next man try his skill. But I fear this task will bring our bravest to despair. Set your hearts upon some other woman: the wife of Odysseus is for the man who is sent by fate and brings the greatest gift."

But Antinous said angrily, " This is hard news for us. Is the bow to bring our bravest to despair because you cannot bend it ? You were never the man to draw a bow, but there are others here who will do the work easily enough." Then he told the goatherd Melanthius to heap up the fire and fetch a round of lard, that they might grease the bow before they tried their skill. So this was done, and the young men tried in turn; but none of them were strong enough. Only Antinous and Eurymachus still held back, and they were the strongest of all.

Now the shepherd and the swineherd rose and left the hall, and Odysseus went out after them; and when they were beyond the gates he said to them, " Friends, there is something I would have you tell me. On whose side would you be, if some God were to bring Odysseus back this very moment ? Would you fight for him, or for the suitors ? Speak out, and tell me the truth." Then the shepherd said, " O that he might come indeed! You should see how my arm could help him." And Eumaeus said the same.

So when Odysseus was sure of their loyalty, he told them, " I am he. I have come home again at last, and none of my household have welcomed me but you. I swear to you that, if I overcome the suitors, you shall be dear to me as my son Telemachus." Then he drew aside his rags, and showed them the scar, where the wild boar had gashed him in his youth. They looked, and knew him, and then they threw their arms about him and kissed him and wept for joy.

But soon he checked them, saying, " Do not weep now, or someone may come out of the hall and see us. Let us go back, one by one, I first, and you after me; and then wait for the signal which I will give. I shall ask you for the bow, and the princes will refuse it; but you must bring it down the hall, my good Eumaeus, and put it in my hands. Then tell the women that they must close the inner doors, and if they should hear groans, or a sound of fighting in the hall, they must not look out, but stay quietly at their work. And it shall be your duty, Philoetius, to shut the gates of the courtyard and make them fast."

Then he went back and sat down in his place by the door, and the two servants went in after him.

By this time Eurymachus had the bow in his hands, and was warming it well before the fire; yet still he could not bend it, and at last he broke out in bitter rage: "Shame on us! On myself, and on us all! It is not so much that I care about the marriage: there are women enough in sea-girt Ithaca and the other lands of Greece. But men will never forget that we were so much weaker than Odysseus that we could not bend his bow."

"It is not so bad as that," said Antinous. "Remember that this is the festival of Apollo, the Archer-God; how could anyone bend a bow to-day? Set it down, and we will leave the axes standing; no one is likely to enter the hall of King Odysseus and carry them away. Then early to-morrow we will tell Melanthius to bring us the best goats from his flock, and we will make a sacrifice to Apollo: and afterwards we will try our skill again and end the match."

Then Odysseus said softly, "Give me a hearing, noble sirs. Let me have the bow, I beg you, since you mean to shoot no more to-day. I should like to see whether I have still my former strength, or whether I have lost it through my wanderings and the hardships I have borne."

But they were angry at that, for they feared he might succeed. "Be silent, fool," said Antinous. "You ought to be content that you can sit among such great lords as we, and listen to our talk. It will only be the worse for you if you bend that bow. Hold your tongue and drink, and do not match yourself with younger men."

But Penelope said, " Antinous, it is not fair or right for anyone here to insult the guests of Telemachus. Do you suppose, even if the stranger should be strong enough to bend the great bow of Odysseus, that he could take me home and make me his wife? No, you need not fear that; he could not hope for it himself."

" Daughter of Icarius," answered Eurymachus, " we do not suppose that he will carry you away. But we should not like some scurrilous rascal to tell how we wooed the wife of a hero, but were too weak to bend his bow; and how a wandering beggar came up and strung it easily. That is how they will talk, and so we shall lose our honour."

" Eurymachus," she said, " it is not in that way your honour is lost. But this stranger is tall and well-set, and says he comes of a worthy stock. Give him the bow and let us see. And if he is able to bend it, I will give him a new cloak and doublet, and a spear and sword, and sandals for his feet, and I will send him wherever he wishes to go."

But Telemachus said, " Mother, the bow is mine, and mine alone, to give or refuse as I will. None of the Greeks should dispute my right, if I chose to give it to the stranger for his own. Go within now, and look after your own work, the loom and the distaff, and see that your maidservants do their tasks. We men will see to the bow, and I above all; for I am master here."

Penelope wondered at him, yet she felt that he

spoke wisely: and she went up to her chamber, where Athena sent sleep to close her eyes.

Meanwhile the swineherd took up the bow, but the princes raised an outcry, and he set it down again. But Telemachus called out threateningly, "Bring the bow here, or I will turn you out of the house. I wish I could get rid of these lords as easily as I could of you." They laughed at the thought and forgot to be angry, so the swineherd brought the bow down the hall and put it in his master's hands. Then he called Eurycleia out from the women's rooms, and said to her, "Telemachus bids you shut the inner doors; and if any of the women should hear groans, or a sound of fighting in the hall, they must not look out, but stay quietly at their work." So the old woman shut the doors.

Then Philoetius sprang up silently and went out, and closed the courtyard-gates. There was a ship's cable lying in the porch: with this he tied the gates fast, and then went back and sat down in his place, with his eyes steady on the king. Meanwhile Odysseus was handling the bow, turning it this way and that, and testing it in every place, to see whether worms had eaten the horns while the master was away from home. And the princes looked at each other, and said, "He has a good enough eye for a bow. The rascal must have the fellow to it at home." But another would say, "If he can bend this one, he is welcome to all he wants."

While they spoke Odysseus had looked to everything; and now, with as little trouble as a minstrel who fits a new cord to his lyre, he bent and strung the mighty bow. He took it in his left hand, and plucked the bowstring, and it rang beneath his touch, clear as a swallow's note. And as he did so Zeus sent a peal of thunder, and the hero's heart leapt at the sound. Fear came on all the suitors, and their faces grew pale. But Odysseus caught up an arrow from the table at his side, and laid it on the centre-piece: he took a steady aim from the stool where he sat, and drew the string, and shot: and the bronze-tipped shaft went clean through all twelve axes from the first one to the last.

Then he called out, " Telemachus, your guest has not disgraced you. I have not missed the mark, and I was not long at the work. The time has come: it is daylight still, but we must give these lords their evening meal, and dance and song shall not be wanting."

At the word he nodded to his son. Then Telemachus slung his sharp sword about him, and grasped his glittering spear.

CHAPTER XXII

HOW ODYSSEUS KILLED THE SUITORS

BUT Odysseus flung off his rags, and sprang to the great threshold with the bow and quiver in his hands. He poured out the arrows at his feet, and shouted to the princes: " So ends the game you could not play! Now for another mark, never hit before!"

With that he shot at Antinous. He, as it chanced, was just lifting a golden cup from the board, never dreaming that death would meet him there, with all his comrades round him at the feast. But before the wine touched his lips, the arrow struck him in the throat, and the cup dropped from his hand, and he fell dying to the floor. The princes sprang to their feet when they saw their comrade fallen, and looked round the walls for armour, but there was not a spear or shield to be found. Then they turned in fury on Odysseus: " Madman, are you shooting at men? You have slain the noblest youth in Ithaca, and you shall not live to draw bow again."

But Odysseus faced them sternly and said, " Dogs, you thought that I should never return. You have rioted in my home, and outraged the women of my household, and you have wooed my own wife while

I was yet a living man. You took no thought for the Gods who rule in heaven, nor for the indignation of men in days hereafter. Now your time has come."

All grew pale as he spoke, and Eurymachus alone found words: "If you are in truth King Odysseus, your words are just: there have been many shameful deeds done upon your lands and in your house. But Antinous, who was the cause of all, lies dead; it was he who led us on, hoping that he might take your kingdom for himself. Spare us now that he has met his doom, for we are your own people; and we will make you full atonement for all that has been eaten and drunk in your halls."

"Eurymachus, you might give me all you have, but even then I would not hold my hands until I had taken vengeance for every wrong. You have your chance. Fight, or fly, if you think that flight can save you."

At that their knees shook beneath them, but Eurymachus cried, "Comrades, this man will have no mercy. He has got the bow in his hands, and he will shoot us down from the threshold, so long as there is one of us left alive. Draw your swords, and guard yourselves with the tables; and let us all set upon him at once and drive him from the doorway. If we can reach the city, we are safe."

As he spoke he drew his sword, and sprang forward with a cry; but at the same moment Odysseus shot. The arrow struck him in the breast, and he dropped forward over the table, while the mist of death sank

on his eyes. Then Amphinomus made a rush for the doorway. But Telemachus was too quick for him: he hurled his spear, and struck him from behind between the shoulders, and he fell crashing on the floor. Telemachus sprang back, leaving the spear, for he dared not wait to draw it out. He darted to his father's side: " Father, we ought to have armour; I will go and get weapons for us."

" Run and bring them," said Odysseus, " while I have arrows left; when these are gone, I cannot hold the doorway against them all."

So Telemachus ran to the armoury, and hurried back with helmets and shields and spears; and he armed himself and made the two servants do the same, and they took their stand beside the king. While the arrows lasted, Odysseus shot, and struck down the wooers man by man. And then he leant the bow against the doorpost, and slung the shield about him, and put on the helmet, and took two spears in his hand.

There was a postern in the hall, close beside the great doorway and opening on the corridor. Odysseus had put the swineherd to guard it, and now the boldest of the suitors said to the rest, " Could not some of us force a passage there, and raise the cry for rescue? "

" Little use in that," said Melanthius, " the great doorway is too close, and one brave man might stop us all before we reached the court. I have a better plan. Odysseus and his son have stowed away the

weapons, and I think I know where they are. I will
go and fetch you what you need."

With the word he clambered up through the
lights of the hall,[1] and got into the armoury, and
fetched out twelve shields and as many spears and
helmets, and brought them to the princes. The
heart of Odysseus misgave him when he saw the
armour; and he felt that the fight would go hard,
and said to Telemachus, " Melanthius or one of
the women has betrayed us."

" Father, it was my fault," said Telemachus, " I
left the door of the armoury open, and one of them
must have kept sharper watch than I did. Go,
Eumaeus, make fast the door, and see if it is the
doing of Melanthius, as I guess."

While they spoke, Melanthius went again to fetch
more armour, and the swineherd spied him and said,
" There is the villain going to the armoury, as we
thought: tell me, shall I kill him, if I can master him,
or shall I bring him here to suffer for his sins? "
" Telemachus and I will guard the doorway," said
Odysseus, " and you and the shepherd shall bind him
hand and foot, and leave him in the chamber to
wait his doom."

So the two went up to the armoury, and stood in
wait on either side of the door; and as Melanthius
came out, they leapt upon him and dragged him
back by the hair and flung him on the ground and
bound him tightly to a pillar hand and foot. " Lie

[1] See Note A at end.

there," said Eumaeus, " and take your ease: the dawn will not find you sleeping, when it is time for you to rise and drive out your goats." With that they went back to join Odysseus, and the four stood together at the threshold, four men against a host.

Then Athena came among them in the likeness of Mentor, and Odysseus knew her and rejoiced. " Mentor," he shouted, " help me in my need, for we are comrades from of old." And the wooers sent up another shout, " Do not listen to him, Mentor: or your turn will come when he is slain." But Athena taunted Odysseus and spurred him to the fight: " Have you lost your strength and courage, Odysseus? It was not thus you did battle for Helen in the ten years' war at Troy. Is it so hard to face the suitors in your own house and home? Come, stand by me, and see if Mentor forgets old friendship." Yet she left the victory still uncertain, that she might prove his courage to the full. She turned herself into a swallow, and flew up into the roof, perching on a blackened rafter overhead.

Then the wooers took courage, when they saw that Mentor was gone, and that the four stood alone in the doorway. And one of them said to the rest, " Let six of us hurl our spears together at Odysseus. If once he falls, there will be little trouble with the rest." So they flung their spears as he bade them: but all of them missed the mark. Then Odysseus gave the word to his men, and they all took steady aim, and threw, and each one killed his man: and the wooers fell back to the further end of the hall, while the four dashed up together, and drew out their spears from the bodies of the slain. Once more the suitors hurled, and Telemachus and the swineherd were wounded: but the other spears fell wide. Then at last Athena lifted her shield of war high overhead, the shield that brings death to men; and panic seized the wooers, and they fled like a drove of cattle when the gadfly stings them, while the four swooped after them like vultures swooping from the clouds; and they fled left and right through the hall, but there was no escape.

Only Phemius the minstrel, whom the wooers had forced to sing before them, sprang forward and clasped the knees of Odysseus, and said, " Have mercy on me, Odysseus: you would not slay a minstrel, who gladdens the hearts of Gods and men? The princes forced me here against my will." And Telemachus heard, and said to his father, " Do not hurt him, for he is not to blame; and let us save the herald too, if he is yet alive, for he took care of me when I was a child."

Now the herald had hidden himself under a stool, and pulled an ox-hide over him, and when he heard this, he crept out and clasped the knees of Telemachus and begged that he would plead for him. " Have no fear," said Odysseus, " my son has saved your life. Go out, you and the minstrel, and wait in the court-yard, for I have other work to do within." So the two went out into the courtyard, and sat down beside the altar, looking for their death each moment.

Then Odysseus searched through the hall, to see if anyone was yet lurking alive. But they all lay fallen in the dust and blood, heaped upon each other, like fishes on a sunny beach when the fisherman has drawn his net to land. Then he told Telemachus to call out the old nurse Eurycleia. She came, and found Odysseus standing among the dead, with his hands and feet all stained with blood: and she was ready to shout for triumph when she saw the great work accomplished. But Odysseus checked her cry, saying, " Keep your joy unspoken, old nurse; there should be no shout of triumph over the slain. It is the judgment of Heaven that has repaid them for the evil deeds they did."

Then he gave orders that the corpses should be carried out and the blood washed away. And when it was done, he turned to Eurycleia and said, " Bring fire and sulphur now, and I will purify the hall. Then bid Penelope meet me here."

" Yes, my child," said the old nurse, " I will obey you. But let me bring you a mantle first: it is not fitting that you should stand here with only your rags to cover you." But Odysseus said that she must do his bidding at once. So she brought sulphur and lit a fire, and Odysseus purified the hall.

CHAPTER XXIII

HOW ODYSSEUS WAS RECOGNISED BY PENELOPE
AT LAST

MEANWHILE the old nurse hurried upstairs to find
Penelope, laughing to herself as she went, and
stumbling in her haste.   And she cried, " Awake,
Penelope, awake, my child, and see with your own
eyes what you have longed for day and night!
Odysseus has come home, and has killed the proud
suitors, who wasted his house and wronged his son."

But Penelope would not believe it, and said,
" Dear nurse, are you out of your mind? How could
you wake me with such a tale, when I was sleeping
so sweetly? It was the sweetest sleep I have ever
had, since Odysseus went away to that fatal land
of Troy. If it had been one of the younger servants
I should have rated her soundly, but I cannot be
angry with you."

But Eurycleia went on, " It is no wild tale, dear
child, it is the sober truth.   Odysseus has really
come. He was that stranger whom they all mocked
and ill-treated in the hall. Telemachus knew it all
the time, but he kept the secret, so that his father
might punish those wicked men."

Then Penelope leapt from the bed, and flung her arms round the nurse's neck: " Tell me, nurse, tell me this! If he has really come, as you say, how could he fight them all alone, one man against a hundred? "

" I did not see it," she answered, " and I do not know, but I heard the groans of the dying. We were all sitting frightened in the inner room, and the doors were shut, until Telemachus summoned us into the hall, and there I found Odysseus standing among the slain. Now he has cleared the hall, and is cleansing the house with brimstone, and there is a great fire on the hearth. He has sent me to fetch you that you may rejoice together, for you have suffered much."

" Dear nurse, do not laugh and boast like that. No one would rejoice so much as his son and I, if it were true. But it cannot be. It must be some God that has slain the suitors and rewarded them for all their sins. No, Odysseus is lost for ever."

" Child, will you never believe? Listen, and I will give you another proof. When I was washing the stranger's feet, I saw the scar of the wound that the wild boar gave him long ago, and I wanted to tell you, but he stopped my mouth. Come with me now, and see if I do not speak the truth, and kill me if I lie."

So they went down together, and as they went, Penelope wondered what she should do when she saw him. And when they entered the hall, she took her seat by the hearth in the firelight, facing Odysseus. He was sitting against a pillar, with his eyes fixed on the ground, waiting for his wife to speak. But she sat there a long while, silent and bewildered. Sometimes she would lift her eyes and look into his face, and then again she doubted him when she saw his rags.

At last Telemachus broke out: " Mother, how can you be so cruel? Why do you not go to my father? No other wife in the world would refuse to speak to her husband, when he had come home at last, after wandering and suffering for twenty years."

" Child," said Penelope, " I am lost in wonder, and I have no power to speak. But if it is really Odysseus, we two have secret signs between us, that no one else can know."

Then Odysseus smiled and said, " Leave her, my son, she will test me later on; for now she cannot see who I am because of this foul clothing that I wear."

Then he took Telemachus aside, and told him that they must prepare to fight against the men of Ithaca, who would come to avenge their friends and kindred, and meanwhile they should sing and dance in the palace to deceive the townsfolk. So Telemachus called the household together, and soon the courts rang with the sound of music and of dancing feet, and the passers-by all said, " So the queen is wedded at last. She could not wait any longer for her husband's return."

Meanwhile Odysseus had bathed and anointed himself with oil, and put on a splendid mantle. And

G 10

Athena made him statelier than before, and his hair fell curling to his shoulders like clustering hyacinths. Then he came back to the hall, and sat down again opposite Penelope, and said to her, "Strange wife, the Gods have given you a harder heart than any woman alive. No other wife would sit like this, apart from her husband, when he had come home to her at last after twenty years of wandering and grief. Come, nurse, make me a bed by myself, for her heart is hard as iron."

And then Penelope spoke at last: "My lord, I am not proud or heartless, nor am I utterly bewildered. But I remember well what you were, when you set sail for Troy in your long-oared ship. Go, nurse, and bring out the good bedstead from the bridal chamber that my husband built, and spread it for him as he bids you."

This she said to try him, but he could bear it no longer, and broke out: "Wife, you cut me to the heart! How could anyone move my bedstead, unless he had learnt my secret? There was a stout olive-tree growing in the inner court, with a stem like a pillar, and I built my chamber round it. I cut off the branches and smoothed the trunk and shaped it into a bed-post, and so built the bedstead there. Does it stand there still, or has any man cut away the olive-stem, and set it up elsewhere?"

Then Penelope could doubt no longer, and her heart was melted when she saw that it was her husband indeed; and she ran to him weeping, and threw her arms round his neck and cried, "Do not be angry with me, Odysseus, that I did not know you at the first, as I know you now. It is the Gods who have kept us apart, and given us sorrow for all these years. And I have always feared that some other man might come and deceive me for his wicked gain. But now you tell me what no one else could know, except my maid and me, and I believe you, and give my heart to you." So Odysseus held in his arms the wife he loved, and wept for joy; and she clung to him, as a tired swimmer clings to the land which he has reached at last after deadly storm and wreck, and her white arms could never quite loose their hold.

And then he said, "Wife, even yet we have not reached the end of all our toils. There are still many labours left which the seer Teiresias foretold, when I went down to the House of Death. So let us now sleep together, and take our rest and joy."

And Penelope answered, "The bed is ready for you whenever you desire. But tell me what this fresh trial is, which the seer foretold, for some day I must know it, and it is better now."

So he replied, "It will give you no joy to hear it, but I will tell you all. He bade me take an oar upon my shoulder, and journey through many lands and cities, till I come to a people who have never heard of the sea, and do not know what an oar is like; and when I meet a man who asks if I have a winnowing-fan on my shoulder, there I must stop, and fix the oar in the ground, and offer sacrifice to King Poseidon. So shall I make my peace with him and with all the Gods, and I shall have rest at last, and my people shall be happy. And death will come to me at last from the sea, the gentlest death of all, when my strength is gone, at the end of a calm old age."

So they talked together, while the bowermaid and the old nurse were preparing their bed by the light of the blazing torches. And when all was ready, the bower-maid led them to their marriage-chamber, torch in hand, as she had led them twenty years before. There they lay down together, and the dancing ceased in the courts of the palace, and the whole house was still.

CHAPTER XXIV

HOW ODYSSEUS AND HIS FATHER MET AGAIN, AND HOW PEACE WAS MADE IN ITHACA

NEXT morning when Odysseus rose, he bade his wife shut herself up in the palace and speak to no one, while he went out to see his father. He girded on his armour and called Telemachus and the two herdsmen, and told them to take their weapons and follow him. So the four set out together, and no one saw them as they went through the town and out into the country. They soon reached the well-kept farm and the little house where the old man lived. He was always alone, except for his labourers and one old faithful woman who served in the house. Odysseus bade the others go indoors and prepare a feast, while he went down to the orchard to look for his father. The men had gone into the fields, and Laertes was by himself, digging round his trees; and there his son found him as he worked in his garden and nursed his grief. He was wearing a rough goatskin cap and leather gloves and gaiters, and his garments were old and patched. Odysseus stood under a tall pear-tree and looked at him, and saw how worn he was with age and sorrow. The tears fell from his eyes, and he yearned to take

his father in his arms and kiss him, and tell him he
had come home at last. But he thought again, and
resolved to speak to him first like a stranger, until
he knew what was in his heart. So he went up and
stood beside him as he bent over his work, and said:

"I see you know how to look after an orchard, old
man. What care you take of every single plant and
tree, fig and olive and pear and vine, and all the
garden herbs! But no one seems to take care of you,
my friend, if I have your leave to say so. Surely
your master can have no cause to neglect you thus
in your old age. And yet you look too tall and noble
for a slave: I should take you for a king, who ought
to sleep soft at night and have ease and comfort and
all the dues of age. Tell me who you are, and who
your master is: and tell me if I have really come to
Ithaca. For I had a guest once, the dearest guest
that ever came to me, and he told me his home was
in Ithaca and that his father was called Laertes. I
loved him like a brother, and when he left me I
gave him splendid gifts, wrought silver and gold and
raiment, and four fair slaves to work for him."

Then Laertes looked up and said, "Yes, stranger,
this is the place. But robbers and usurpers are in
possession of the land, and there is no one now to
welcome you as you deserve, and as he would have
done had you found him here alive. But tell me, my
friend, tell me this! How long is it since you saw
that guest of yours? He was my son, and I fear he
must have perished now, far away from us all, with

out father or mother or wife to weep over him and close his eyes."

"It must be five years now," said Odysseus, "since he left me. Alas! we parted so hopefully, and thought we should meet again and be guest and host once more."

Then darkness and sorrow fell upon Laertes, and he took dust and ashes in his hands and poured them on his grey hairs, weeping bitterly. And when Odysseus saw it, his heart smote him for pity, and he felt the sting and throb of the rising tears and could not keep them back. He flung his arms round his father and kissed him, crying, "Father, I am here, I have come back to you at last! Do not grieve any more, for I have won the victory and slain the suitors in my halls."

Then Laertes said, "If you are indeed my son Odysseus, give me a sign that I may know it."

"See, here is the scar of the old wound from the wild boar's tusk. And I can tell you every tree you gave me on this very ground when I was a little lad. I used to follow you round the orchard and ask you for them, and you would tell me their names and choose out some to be my own. Ten apple-trees you gave me, and thirteen pears, and forty figs, and you said I was to have fifty rows of vines just here, that would all be covered with grapes when Zeus sent the heavy showers and made them grow."

Then Laertes saw that it was true, and he stretched out his hands to his son. But his knees trembled

beneath him, and he sank fainting, and would have
fallen, had not Odysseus caught him in his arms and
held him to his breast. But after a little while the
old man's strength returned, and he raised himself
and cried, " O Father Zeus! Now I know indeed
that thou reignest on Olympus, if vengeance has
been taken on the wooers for their sins! Yet I am
afraid the men of Ithaca will set upon us now, and
send for help to the islanders."

" Courage, father," answered Odysseus, " there is
no need for fear. But let us go in and meet Telemachus: I sent him on with the herdsmen and told
them to prepare a feast."

So the two went in together. And the old dame
met them at the door and took Laertes to the bath
and he anointed himself and put on a splendid mantle
and came back to the hall, and he seemed to have
grown tall and strong again and stately as an Immortal, so that Odysseus gazed at him in joy and
said, " Father, one of the everlasting Gods must have
touched you, and given you strength and grace."

" Oh, if they could give me the strength of my
youth!" he answered. "If I could have stood beside you yesterday, when you faced the suitors in
our halls, and helped you in the work!"

So they talked and rejoiced together. Meanwhile
the old woman had gone out to call the labourers
and they came up to the hall, but when they reached
the threshold they stopped and stood still, dumb
with wonder at what they saw. But Odysseus caught

sight of them and said to the oldest, who had been his servant once, "Come in, my friend, come in. We have been waiting a long while for you." Then the old man rushed up to him and seized his hand and kissed it, blessing the Gods because they had brought his master home at last.

Meanwhile, Rumour was up and abroad through the town, flying everywhere with the tidings that the suitors had been foully slain. Their friends and kinsfolk gathered together and carried away the corpses from the palace-gate, weeping over their dead, till their hearts grew hot for vengeance. The father of Antinous, Eupeithes, took the lead, and spoke to the people in the market-place:

"Hear what your king has done! He took your ships, and sailed away with your stoutest warriors twenty years ago, and brought them all to ruin, and now he has come back and slaughtered the noblest of our youth. Shall we take no vengeance for our children and our friends? I would rather die and follow my son. Up, and kill the tyrant!"

Then the people pitied his grief; yet some of them murmured and said the suitors had deserved their death, and others told how the Gods had stood beside Odysseus and helped him in the fight. But Eupeithes won most of them to his side, and they seized their weapons and shouted that they would follow him, and he led the way to Laertes' farm.

But far above, on the heights of Olympus, Athena spoke to her father Zeus: "Tell me, my father,

*G

what is your will? Shall we waken the terrible war-
cry or make peace between the two?"

And the Cloud-gatherer smiled and said, "Have
you not guided Odysseus from the first? Choose
yourself what should be done. Yet I would have
them make a covenant together, so that they forget their anger and bitterness, and love each other
as they did before, and there shall be peace and
plenty in the land."

Meanwhile the feast was over in Laertes' hall, and
Odysseus rose and said, "One of you go out and see
if they are coming now." Then one of the servants
went out, but ran back at once, crying, "Quick, arm
yourselves! They are here already."

Upon that they grasped their weapons, and even
the old Laertes buckled on his armour, for their
force was small; and they flung open the doors, and
rushed out with Odysseus at their head. "You will
bear yourself like a man, I know," he said to Telemachus, "and remember the honour of our race."
And Telemachus answered, "Father, I will no
shame you." And Laertes heard them and cried,
"A proud day for me, when my son and my son's
son outdo one another in deeds of valour!"

Then he poised his spear and hurled it at Eupeithes.
It struck through the helmet and down he crashed in
the dust. At that Odysseus and Telemachus leapt on
the foremost fighters and would have slain them all.
But Athena shot down from the peaks of Olympus
and her voice rang out above the fray:

" Back, men of Ithaca! Back, and fight no more! "

At the cry of the Goddess they turned pale, and the weapons dropped from their hands, and they fled away in fear. Odysseus shouted, and dashed after in pursuit as an eagle swoops from the sky.

But Athena touched him and said, " Son of Laertes, hold your hand and shed no blood, or you will anger Father Zeus whose eyes are over all." And Odysseus heard her voice, and obeyed her gladly.

Thus Athena, the grey-eyed Goddess, stopped the fight, and afterwards she made a faithful covenant between them, and they lived in peace together.

APPENDIX

APPENDIX

APPENDIX

THE HOMERIC PROBLEM

THESE little books do not profess to be more than shortened and simplified versions of the great poetic originals, and they are designed, in the first instance, for children. There seemed to us good reasons for attempting such a task. The *Iliad* and the *Odyssey* are among those masterpieces, comparatively few, that are full of matter appealing alike to the old and the very young. But not only has a complete rendering of the poems as they stand in the Greek defied the skill of every modern translator : even if complete translation were successful beyond hope, the poems are too long and too complicated to be put into the hands of children. Yet most of the stories in themselves are so beautiful and so simple that they may well take their place among the first that a child is told. But, besides the length, there are other difficulties in the poems as they stand.

In the first place the diction is too richly adorned to be easily understood by children; and in the next, the poems in their present form, especially the *Iliad*, show clearly enough that several poets have been at work on the main theme, with results that may sometimes enrich, but more often, however fine in themselves, are apt to weaken or obscure the magnificent outlines of the first great plot. Such, at least, is the opinion now dominant among scholars, and it is shared by the present translators. Over and above simplifying the diction, we have therefore made, deliberately, large cuts in the subject-matter. For the *Iliad* most of these are indicated by notes at the end of the volume, with the chief reasons for making them. For the *Odyssey* they are too few to be worth noting.

The growth of the Homeric poems has been, and is likely to be, a constant subject of dispute if only because the known facts are extremely scanty. But it is safe enough to say that the Greeks of the classic period were familiar with them, much in their present form, at the time of Peisistratus, tyrant of Athens in the 6th century B.C.

For this we have fairly good evidence, while the absence of any reference to the Greek colonies in Asia Minor makes it extremely probable that the plot of the *Iliad*, as composed by the first masterhand, takes us back to at least the 9th century, and it is likely that we ought to go back farther still. Recent discoveries, especially in Crete, at Mycenae, and at Troy itself, have brought to light traces of a high civilisation in the Aegaean basin, growing up from neolithic times, a civilisation the details of which were forgotten by classical Greece, and

which is both like and unlike that implied in the
Iliad and the *Odyssey*.

Many points in the Homeric poems are directly
illustrated by the archæological finds: for example
Hector's long shield in the *Iliad* with the black rim
tapping at his heels; and the inlaid pictures on the
armour of Achilles. Again, the prominence given in
the poems to "golden Mycenae," a deserted site in
classical days, and to the ancient glories of Crete,
an island outside the main stream of classic expan-
sion, accord strikingly with the dominance of these
centres in the age of the buildings and treasures
now revealed.

On the other hand, there are differences almost
equally striking. The dress of the women is mark-
edly different, much of the armour is different,
Homer speaks of the "fair-haired Achaians," while
the Cretans are all shown in the paintings as dark-
haired, and, what is perhaps more important, the
huge Cretan palaces and the scenes in their frescoes
indicate a far more elaborate life than Homer's.
This appears the more significant when we remember
the contrast drawn in the *Odyssey* between men like
the hero himself, accustomed to a hardy life in the
rough island that was "a good nurse of heroes," and
the Sea-kings in their island paradise, men who are
indeed ready to accept Odysseus as fit to mate with
their princess, who understand his language and
appreciate his fame, but are also at once far beyond
him and his in the material arts of civilisation, and

already touched, it would appear, with something like decadence, indolent and luxurious, loving over-much the dance and the lute, the warm bath and sleep.

The presumption follows that the Homeric poems took their rise in an age of transition between the bloom of this old Aegaean civilisation, a bloom which may be dated roughly between 1600 and 1100 B.C., and the first founding of the Greek cities in Asia Minor, some time, say, during the 11th or 10th century. The poems, we may conjecture, were composed by men related to the makers of that earlier culture, but not to be identified with them. How exactly they were related we cannot say. We do not know whether the Cretans were Indo-Europeans or not, still less whether they were Greek, while it is generally agreed that the new-comers were Greek, coming down from the North-West, and that the poems (in anything like their present form) were composed in Greek. But it may turn out that the Cretans themselves were of the same great branch as the new-comers, Indo-Europeans who had pressed down from the North beyond the Danube to the sunny islands and peninsulas of the South.

That there was a time of profound change in the Aegaean about the 12th century or earlier is suggested by many facts. The great palaces in Crete are found burnt, presumably by a victorious enemy, the beautiful old pottery becomes debased in design and workmanship, the sign-script disappears.

On the site of Troy itself (Hissarlik), a stately city has been laid bare, the sixth from the bottom of successive foundations, and the remains indicate that this city too was overthrown in war. Above it are only traces of much later and more meagre building. The date of this city agrees, so far as we can tell, with the splendid days of Mycenae, and it is now generally believed that the campaign against Troy was a real historic fact. And, whatever truth may lie in the romantic tale of Helen and Paris, there is reason for thinking that larger causes, economic and military, were also at work.

The passage of the Dardanelles has been, all through the ages and up to our own days, of the utmost importance both for Asia Minor and Southern Europe. Here is the natural trade-route with Russia and the natural bridge between East and West. Troy held that key in early days, Byzantium (Constantinople) has held it ever since. It is not unreasonable to suppose that a great expedition to capture this invaluable centre set out from the mainland of Greece and the islands, when Mycenae still had much of her old prestige, though younger and sturdier stocks from the North and North-West (such as are indicated by Achilles of Phthia and Odysseus of Ithaca) would soon be in a position to dispute her primacy. In the confusion that followed the long Trojan war, a confusion suggested more than once in the *Odyssey*, the old centres may well have gone under, with many of their character-

istic features, while the new structures of classical
Greece were rising on, and higher than, the early
foundations.

The *Odyssey*, it has often been noticed, is full of
the colonising spirit, and we have already spoken of
the Greek colonies in Asia Minor that usher in the
classic age. Tradition pointed to Asia Minor itself
as the birthplace of the Homeric poets, and there
may be truth after all in the legend that the sweetest
singer of them all was the " blind old bard of Chios'
rocky isle."

Our translations are illustrated by drawings taken
from the vase-paintings of classic Greece. The
splendid pottery of Crete was never painted with
human figures, but with designs—more or less con-
ventionalised—suggested by flowers and sea-creatures.
But as this exquisite art passed away, its place was
taken by another, at first wofully crude, where the
figures of men and women were of chief interest. As
the new art advanced, these figures were, as a rule,
painted in polished black glaze on the fine red sur-
face of the pottery, and later, the main body of the
pot was covered with the black glaze, with the out-
line of the figures left in a silhouette of red, helped by
black lines for the details. Most of our illustrations
are from these later " red-figured " vases. We have
given no titles to the pictures, because, in the first
place, the Greek vase-painters felt themselves quite
at liberty to vary the details of the subject they
wished to illustrate, and, in the next, we have some-

times chosen figures which seemed to us beautiful and apt, but which there is no reason for supposing were intended to represent Homeric subjects.

Of complete versions the following may be found of most use:—

Chapman's *Homer*, the famous Elizabethan rendering that inspired Keats.

Pope's *Homer*.

Worsley's *Odyssey*.

William Morris's *Odyssey*.

Lang, Leaf and Myers's *Iliad*.

Butcher and Lang's *Odyssey*. The last two in literal prose.

For books of reference:—

Homer. Jebb.

Homer and the Epic. A. Lang.

Rise of the Greek Epic. G. Murray.

The Discoveries in Crete. Burrows.

Schliemann's Excavations. Schuchhardt.

PRONOUNCING LIST OF PROPER NAMES

THE table below indicates how the difficult proper names are usually pronounced in English. Long vowels are marked by the sign ‾, diphthongs by the circumflex, ⌢, and accented syllables by the acute accent, ´. The vowels and consonants have their usual English sound. *G* is always hard.

Achaians	= A-kí-ans	Antenor	= An-té-nor
Achilles	= A-kill-ēs	Anthemion	= Anth-ém-i-on
Admetus	= Ad-mé-tus	Antilochus	= An-tíl-ok-us
Aegaean	= Ē-jé-an	Antimachus	= An-tím-ak-us
Aegisthus	= Ē-jísth-us	Antinous	= An-tín-o-us
Aeneas	= E-né-as	Antiphus	= Án-ti-fus
Aeolus	= Ē-ol-us	Aphrodite	= Af-ro-dí-tē
Aetolia	= Ē-tó-li-a	Ares	= Á-rēs
Agamemnon	= Ág-a-mém-non	Arete	= A-ré-tē
Agenor	= Ag-é-nor	Argos	= Ár-gos
Ajax	= Á-jax	Argive	= Árg-īve
Alcinous	= Al-sín-o-us	Ariadne	= Ar-i-ád-nē
Alkimus	= Ál-kim-us	Artemis	= Árt-em-is
Amphinomus	= Am-fín-om-us	Asius	= Ás-i-us
Anchises	= An-kí-sēs	Asteropaius	= As-ter-o-pí-us
Andromache	= An-dróm-ak-ē	Astynous	= As-tín-o-us
Anticleia	= An-ti-klí-a	Athena	= Ath-é-na
Anteia	= An-tí-a	Atreus	= Át-reûs

215

Automedon	= Aw-tóm-e-don	Delos	= Dé-los
Autonous	= Aw-tón-o-us	Deiphobus	= Dē-íf-ob-us
		Democoon	= Dē-mók-o-on
Bellerophon	= Bèll-ér-of-on	Demoleon	= Dē-mól-e-on
Bienor	= Bi-é-nor	Diomede	= Dī-o-mḗd
Boeotian	= Bē-ṓ-shi-an	Dolops	= Dól-ops
Bouprasion	= Bōō-prás-i-on	Dryops	= Drý-ops
Boötes	= Bo-ṓ-tēs	Dymas	= Dý-mas
Briseis	= Brī-sé-is		
		Echeclus	= Ek-ék-lus
Calchas	= Kál-kas	Echepolus	= Ek-e-pól-us
Caletus	= Kal-é-tus	Elephenor	= El-e-fé-nor
Centaurs	= Sén-tors	Elis	= É-lis
Charis	= Ká-ris	Epeius	= E-pí-us
Charops	= Ká-rops	Epirus	= E-pír-us
Chimaera	= Ki-mḗer-a	Eumaeus	= U-mé-us
Chiron	= Kí-ron	Eumelus	= U-mḗ-lus
Charybdis	= Ka-ríb-dis	Eupeithes	= U-pí-thēs
Chryses	= Krī-sēs	Euphorbus	= U-fór-bus
Chryseis	= Krī-sḗ-is	Euryalus	= U-rí-al-us
Cimmerians	= Sim-mér-ri-ans	Eurybates	= U-ríb-at-ēs
Circe	= Sír-sē	Eurycleia	= U-ry-klí-a
Cleitus	= Klí-tus	Eurylochus	= U-ríl-ok-us
Cleoboulus	= Kle-o-bōō-lus	Eurymachus	= U-rím-ak-us
Clytemnestra	=	Eurynome	= U-rín-om-ē
	Kly-tem-nést-ra	Eurypylus	= U-ríp-il-us
Clytius	= Klít-i-us		
Coiranus	= Kói-ran-us	Glaucus	= Gláw-kus
Cranae	= Krán-a-ē		
Cronos	= Krón-os	Hecuba	= Hék-u-ba
Cyclops	= Sý-klops	Helenus	= Hél-en-us
		Hera	= Hér-a
		Heracles	= Hér-a-klēs
Daedalus	= Dé-dal-us	Hermes	= Hérm-ēs
Dardanus	= Dár-dan us	Hephaestus	= He-féest-us

Hyades	= Hý-ad-ēs	Machaon	= Mak-á-on
Hyperion	= Hy-pér-i-on	Malea	= Mál-e-a
Hippodamas	= Hipp-ód-am-as	Medon	= Méd-on
Hippolochus	= Hipp-ól-ok-us	Meges	= Még-ēs
Hippothous	= Hipp-óth-o-us	Melanippus	= Mél-an-ípp-us
		Melanthius	= Mel-ánth-i-us
Icarius	= Ī-cár-i-us	Menelaus	= Mén-e-lá-us
Idomeneus	= Ī-dóm-en-eûs	Menestheus	= Men-ésth-eûs
Ilium	= Í-li-um	Mentes	= Mén-tēs
Ilus	= Í-lus	Meriones	= Mer-í-on-ēs
Iphidamas	= Ī-fíd-am-as	Merops	= Mér-ops
Iphition	= Ī-fít-i-on	Mycenae	= My-sé-nē
Iris	= Í-ris	Myrmidon	= Múr-mid-on
Irus	= Í-rus	Mysians	= Mís-i-ans
Isandrus	= Is-ánd-rus		
Isus	= Í-sus	Nausicaa	= Naw-sík-a-a
Ithaca	= Íth-ak-a	Neleus	= Né-leûs
		Nereid	= Nér-e-id
Jason	= Já-son	Niobe	= Ní-o-bē
Kebriones	= Keb-rí-on-ēs	Odysseus	= Od-ýss-eûs
Koon	= Kó-ōn	Oedipus	= É-dip-us
		Oileus	= O-í-leûs
Lacedaemon	= Lás-e-dé-mon	Olympus	= Ol-ýmp-us
Laertes	= La-ért-ēs		
Laodamas	= La-ód-am-as	Paionian	= Pī-ón-i-an
Laodameia	= Lá-od-a-mí-a	Pallas	= Pál-las
Laodica	= La-ód-ik-a	Pandarus	= Pán-dar-us
Leiocritus	= Lī-ók-rit-us	Panopeus	= Pán-op-eûs
Leitus	= Lé-it-us	Patroclus	= Pa-trók-lus
Leucas	= Léu-kas	Peirithous	= Pī-ríth-o-us
Lycaon	= Lik-á-on	Peirus	= Pí-rus
Lycia	= Lísh-i-a	Pelasgians	= Pe-lásg-i-ans
Lycomede	= Lík-o-mēd	Pelion	= Pé-li-on

Peleus	= Pḗ-leũs	Scylla	= Sýl-la
Penelope	= Pē-nél-op-ē	Sidonian	= Sī-dṓ-ni-an
Periphas	= Pér-i-fas	Simoeis	= Sím-o-īs
Persephone	= Per-séf-on-ē	Socus	= Sō-kus
Phemius	= Fē-mi-us	Solymi	= Sól-y-mi
Philoetius	= Fil-ḗ-ti-us	Sthenelus	= Sthén-el-us
Phoebus	= Fḗ-bus		
Phoenician	= Fē-nísh-i-an		
Phocian	= Fṓ-shi-an	Talthybius	= Tal-thýb-i-us
Phorkys	= Fór-kys	Teiresias	= Tī-rés-i-as
Phthia	= Fthí-a	Telemachus	= Tē-lém-ak-us
Pleiades	= Plí-ad-ēs	Teucer	= Teũ-ser
Polites	= Pol-í-tēs	Thalusius	= Thal-ū́-si-us
Polyctor	= Pol-ík-tor	Theano	= The-á-no
Polydamas	= Pol-íd-am-as	Thebes	= Thḗbs
Polydeuces	= Pol-y-deũs-ēs	Theoclymenus	=
Polydorus	= Pol-y-dṓr-us		The-o-klým-en-us
Polyphemus	= Pol-y-fē-mus	Theseus	= Thés-eũs
Poseidon	= Pos-í-don	Thetis	= Thét-is
Priam	= Prí-am	Thoas	= Thó-as
Proitus	= Prṓi-tus	Thrasymede	= Thrás-y-mēd
Proteus	= Prṓ-teũs	Troilus	= Trṓi-lus
		Tros	= Trós
Sarpedon	= Sar-pē-don	Tydeus	= Tý̄-deũs
Scaian	= Skí-an		
Scamander	= Ska-mán-der	Zeus	= Zeũs

NOTES

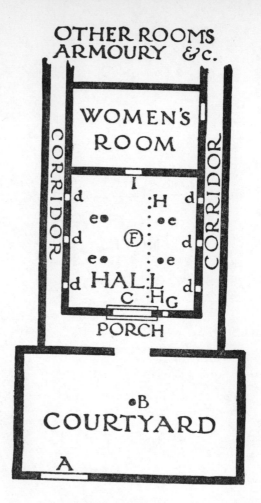

NOTE A

A.   Courtyard Gates.

B.   Altar in Courtyard.

C.   Great Threshold, probably of stone with wooden
        fittings.

d d.   The " Lights of the Hall " (through which Melanthius
        climbed). These we suppose to have been small
        openings high up in the walls.

e e.   Pillars.

F.   Hearth.

G.   Postern.

H H.   Line of Axes.

I.   Inner Doors leading to Women's Room.

NOTE B

The axes had holes pierced in their blades. The twelve
would be set upright, one directly behind the other, with the
handles fixed in the ground; and the arrow, if shot straight,
could pass right through the line of holes. A pierced axe-
blade of the kind meant has been found in an ancient tomb
near Sparta.